TALKING HEALTH, SAFETY AND WELLBEING

The book considers what makes an excellent face-to-face health and safety contact in the workplace, and why these contacts are a fundamental building block of any strong, caring, and empowering workplace culture. It stresses the vital importance of inquiry, empathy, and analysis in understanding what employees need to mitigate risk factors around safety and mental health.

This revised and updated edition includes empowering methodologies that directly address mental health and well-being issues and the challenges organisations face in a post COVID19 era. The reader will gain an understanding of the day-to-day mechanisms of why "culture is king" and how everyone contributes every-day to this truism. This book covers how interactions regarding leadership and teamwork directly lead to the amount of human error and fallibility an organisation can expect to need to manage, and how taking proactive, analytical, and empowering approaches to safety and health is key to identifying and mitigating risks.

Talking Health, Safety and Wellbeing explains why it is so important to talk about health and safety issues proactively. Written in an accessible and engaging manner, this book is an ideal read for any frontline supervisor, HR manager, mental health first aider, safety rep, or company director.

Tim Marsh is considered a world authority on behavioural safety, and has worked with over 500 companies worldwide, including Shell, Pfizer, and BBC. He has delivered dozens of keynote talks all around the world and written several books and hundreds of articles.

D1611096

'The relationship between worker psychological health and work-place safety has been avoided for far too long by researchers and practitioners alike. Tim's blue pie model describes this relationship in a way that is easy to understand. People looking for the next "step-change" in safety can use it to address the psychological health of the workforce.'

Joelle Mitchell, Producer, Psych Health and Safety Global Podcast

'For many years "safety" has been singularly analogous with improving "health and safety" performance. When the reality is – as Tim portrays so effectively in his books and talks – is that only by adopting a holistic approach to reducing risk; addressing human behaviours and wellbeing, can we truly deliver sustainable and optimal performance.'

Steve Booker, Former Global Head of Risk, CBRE Data Centre Solutions

'When I first read *Talking Health, Safety and Wellbeing* it spoke to me; Tim articulates this complex area in a user-friendly way. As a result, during mental health awareness week, we engaged Tim to present to our teams, supply chain, and key clients and contacts. The presentation was thoroughly engaging and did justice to this hugely important topic, linking mental health and human behaviours to safety. It sparked debate, reflection, and, most importantly, raised awareness. I thoroughly recommend Tim's human-centred, impactful, holistic, and integrated approach to addressing the major causes of human error.'

Laura Thomas, Legal and QHSE Director, Jackson Civil Engineering

'Tim's unique writing style makes his content utterly compelling and engaging to all. You always come away asking yourself questions about what you have read and are left wanting more.'

Ian Hart, Editor, *Safety and Health Practitioner*

TALKING HEALTH, SAFETY AND WELLBEING

BUILDING AN EMPOWERING CULTURE
IN A POST-COVID WORLD

3rd Edition

Tim Marsh

Routledge
Taylor & Francis Group

LONDON AND NEW YORK

Third edition published 2022
by Routledge
2 Park Square, Milton Park, Abingdon, Oxon, OX14 4RN

and by Routledge
605 Third Avenue, New York, NY 10158

Routledge is an imprint of the Taylor & Francis Group, an informa business

First edition published by Gower Publishing 2014
Second edition published by Routledge 2017

British Library Cataloguing-in-Publication Data
A catalogue record for this book is available from the British Library

Library of Congress Cataloging-in-Publication Data
A catalog record for this book has been requested

ISBN: 978-1-032-01231-5 (hbk)
ISBN: 978-1-032-00630-7 (pbk)
ISBN: 978-1-003-17778-4 (ebk)

DOI: 10.4324/9781003177784

The first edition of the original book was dedicated to 'the wonderful couple, married 56 years now, who my children call Nanny Babs and Grandad'. Make that 65 years now – complete with personal letter from the Queen of the UK!

(I'm a Republican but my parents aren't and, more than that, even I can see that the Queen is a woman who, thrust into the role with no choice, has done an excellent and highly professional job for a very long time. So, two examples of the excellence and resilience this book is all about and we're still on the dedication!)

WE HAVE 'NO NAME, NO BLAME' REPORTING ON THIS PLATFORM– IT'S JUST THAT MANAGEMENT REALLY LIKES TO KNOW WHO IT IS THEY'RE NOT BLAMING
ROGER BEALE

Contents

Contents

Figures

About the author

Tim Marsh, Honorary Professor at the University of Plymouth, was one of the team leaders of the original UK research into behavioural safety in the early 1990s. He has been a chartered psychologist since 1994, and was made a Chartered Fellow of IOSH in 1996. Since then, he has worked with more than 500 organisations around the world, including the European Space Agency and the BBC. He specialises in human error and organisational culture assessment and change. His first major project was with the UK MOD, where he researched recruit suicidal behaviour. For many years, Tim ran the open courses on behavioural safety and safety culture for IOSH, was awarded a 'President's Commendation' in 2008 by the International Institute of Risk and Safety Management, and was selected to be their first-ever 'Specialist Fellow' in 2010. The author of several bestselling books, he has contributed dozens of articles to international magazines, including *Safety and Health Practitioner* (now *IOSH Magazine*) and *Health and Safety at Work* (now *Sentinel*). Tim has a reputation as a lively and engaging speaker, and has chaired and presented keynote talks at dozens of conferences around the world. In 2013, he was invited to give the keynote 'Warner Address' at the 60th BOHS International Conference, and in 2016, he was invited to give the closing keynote at the Campbell Institute's inaugural 'International Thought Leadership' event.

Anker and Marsh Limited can be contacted via their website: www.ankerandmarsh.com.

Preface

This first version of this book was intended as a response to feedback about my book *Affective Safety Management*, and was intended as a stand-alone piece for the number of readers whose view was:

> *A standard safety leadership book of 250 plus pages with a few nice cartoons is all very well for people interested in the subject but I could do with something that I can give to line management that is more concise and tells us exactly what to do for 'a first step'? Minimum theory, just what to do for the first step . . . what to do if we don't do anything else?*

Since then, the safety world has turned sharply towards the world of health, mental health, and wellbeing. Not before time – tired, disengaged, distracted, and pre-occupied people have more accidents as well as being less likely to be productive; it's always been a hugely interrelated field – these concerns have simply seldom been treated as relevant to safety, and in recent years I've striven to encourage organisations to take a genuinely interrelated approach to human error. The good news is that this doesn't make things any more complex. Less complex, if anything. So, whilst this book is longer than the original, it isn't all that much longer.

As ever, the 80:20 principle applies. If you only do 'step one' *well*, you'll achieve the fabled step change of a 50 per cent reduction in the most visible key performance indicator (KPI): accidents. More than that, doing this well will directly impact the key KPIs of wellbeing and mental health, resulting in less absenteeism and presenteeism; less turnover – especially of key staff; more engagement; more 'citizenship' (or discretionary) behaviours such as 'brother's keeper' acts; and more creativity. I absolutely *guarantee* it. (And I absolutely guarantee that if you cost the $

and £ data impacted by these KPIs, you'll have a headline figure for that opening slide that will get you the full attention of even the most cold-hearted CFO).

There has to be a little theory for background, I'm afraid. As the book explains, few people will engage with gusto if you don't explain 'why' as well as 'what' – but I've aimed to keep that as user-friendly as possible. There's lots of further reading suggested if you wish to delve more deeply.

Two stories and a case study by way of introduction

If you'll allow me a little indulgence, I'd like to start with some stories to introduce myself and the book. Two of the three are entirely true.

The first refers to a Welsh rugby legend, Bobby Windsor, who was a neighbour of mine in South Wales. Indeed, my father, who was a teacher, taught him at school. Bobby was part of the famous Pontypool front row that toured South Africa successfully in 1974 with the British Lions rugby team – a famous series win!

In those days there were no mobile phones, of course, and a team meeting was called to sort out the problem of someone continually sneaking into the management's rooms to make (expensive) phone calls home.

The management got the squad together and offered the offender the chance to confess.

Nothing.

They pointed out that all the calls were to the same number, and that it was a *Pontypool* number . . .

At which Bobby leapt to his feet spun around and shouted 'Right! Which one of you bastards has been phoning my wife!?'

The moral: there are times when you've taken a risk when you'll need to think on your feet.

The second story is about my Aunt Shirley who was pulled over for speeding by a young PC. He asked to see her driving licence, but she said she didn't have one.

He asked if it was even her car that she was driving, but she said no, it belonged to a Tom Jukes. She was asked if Mr Jukes had lent her the car, and she said that no, she'd stolen it, but only after she'd killed Tom, chopped him up, and put him in the boot.

Shaken, the young PC seized her car keys and called for backup. Presently a senior officer arrived and took charge of the situation. 'Please step to the boot and open it, madam', he said. My aunt did so. The boot was empty.

'Interesting', he said, and then asked, 'Could I see your driver's licence, please?' She said, 'Certainly', and handed it over. 'Is this your car?', he asked. 'Yes, officer. Would you like to see the log book?'

'No need for that', said the officer, 'but this is really very interesting. My young officer over there told me that you don't have a driving licence and that this isn't your car. Indeed, he says that you stole this car from a Mr Tom Jukes who you'd just killed, chopped up, and put in the boot here'.

My aunt's response: 'Oh, the lying little bugger! I can only hope he's not gone and told you I was *speeding* as well!' (Same moral!)

AND YOUR POINT IS?! YOU MAY WELL ASK . . .

You may be thinking that these two so-called 'learning points' can't possibly underpin a safety and health book, and you'd be right, of course. As ever, with a psychologist, you just can't trust them and there's a hidden agenda.

What I've tried to do here are the following four things:

- To amuse you. Simply because if you're smiling, that's a good thing in itself, and the truth that 'laughter is the best medicine' was never more true than in the early 2020s as we deal with the trauma of Covid-19 and 'long Covid' issues.
- But also to try surprise you pleasantly, and to get you thinking, 'Well, so far, this read is going a lot better than I thought it would!'

- 'Step One' of a safety and health talk, as below, is to 'introduce yourself, break the ice and set the right tone', and I've tried, in my own fashion, to model that here.
- Finally, to illustrate a fundamental principle. I hope you laughed at the two stories above, which are essentially about getting away with theft and speeding! You see, as a species, we don't just have a level of risk tolerance – we each have a level of risk *appetite* that we are born with.

Basically, as a species, we rather like to push our luck.

Make a playground too safe, and small children will adapt it to make it more dangerous – they'll climb *over it* rather than through it. They'll swing from it and jump off it. It's part of what makes us such a wildly successful species. We like to master risk, as it makes us feel in control of our environment – or maybe just because we like the way it revs us up and gets our blood flowing, and we very often laugh at 'naughty'.

In short, if we're to effectively address human error and fallibility around health and safety issues, we have to address human nature as it actually is; there are times when individuals and organisations could be rather more risk savvy than they often are, in the safety field and in the health and wellbeing field. This book seeks to help with that.

CASE STUDY

Some years ago, a client asked me to come up with the 'best behavioural safety programme known to man' following a mistake by an engineer that closed a major airport, made the evening news, and cost hundreds of millions. We quickly agreed that this was a human error project, not a safety project. They reviewed the many excellent HE courses, but found them 'often too theoretical and descriptive'. (If you're unfamiliar, the human error 'dirty dozen' is a great place to start. It covers communication, distraction, resources, knowledge, stress, complacency, team work, pressure, awareness, fatigue, lack of assertion, and norms and is very easy to search up on the web). They said they wanted something more proactive than a 'be aware of these issues' approach. ('You know, a full-on culture change programme'.)

We visited several sites, then reconvened. Discussing an engineer we'd just met, the client challenged, 'Can you imagine if Bob fell down the stairs in the middle of the night . . . then something happened and he couldn't raise the alarm or respond?' (To an outage or some such.) My observation was, 'Quite – but you do know that Bob is about 35 times more likely to *throw* himself down the stairs than fall down them?', quoting the ratio of industrial fatalities to suicides of working people from the UK. Then I added, 'Of course, if he got vindictive and ran amok with an axe for 30 minutes first . . .' The client considered this, checked the figures I'd quoted, then went white. Literally. We quickly agreed our human error programme would address all the major root causes of human error as proactively as possible – mental health included.

Before we parted, the client commented, 'You don't think one of our engineers is likely to do that, do you?' I said, 'Well, one of them might. He's just split up with his wife, is distraught about it, is sleeping on a friend's couch, and is drinking more than he did when he was 20 . . . and none of his colleagues has a clue, because he always puts on a brave face and they are all middle-aged, male *engineers* who have actively volunteered to work the solitary night shift. No one would ever ask about his mental health!' He thought about this for a bit too, then asked, 'But why did he tell you all that when he'd only just met you?' The reply is, of course, a lead-in to the rest of the book. 'I asked him how he was, as not surprisingly he'd sounded a bit edgy, and when he started to talk, I kept listening. I imagine he's been desperate to talk to someone for a while, and I was simply the first person to give him the opportunity'.

Safety, wellbeing, mental health, even productivity: good-quality dialogue helps them all.

It's good to talk.

Introduction

This book is divided into two relatively short sections. The first section addresses the reasons why so many organisations undertake some form of 'walk and talk' process. It summarises the most recent thinking and innovation, but assumes no prior knowledge, so covers first principles. This is because experience shows that a lot of people who have been tasked to undertake these safety and health conversations for years haven't had this explained to them!

It covers:

- Why compliance is not even half the story.
- Why day-to-day behaviour is so important.
- Why 'try hard to make fewer mistakes and to take more care of yourself' can't ever work.
- What world class health and safety leadership looks like *generally*.

Its basic aim is to establish why a dedicated 'walk and talk' is so important to developing a strong safety and health culture, and therefore in minimising the amount of unsafe and unhealthy behaviour in an organisation.

The second section addresses, in the light of these theories and principles, the practicalities of what a really good conversation contains. The suggested model contains just the five steps, which are:

- Introducing yourself, breaking the ice, and setting the tone.
- Objective analysis and learning.
- Coaching.
- Eliciting a promise?
- Closing out.

DOI: 10.4324/9781003177784-1

The aim is to make the book as logical and user-friendly as it can be, so where it seemed appropriate, there are some practical lists in the background section and some background in the practical section.

Before we start, I'd like to tell you another story – this one illustrating perfectly the sort of dedication I so often see in the safety community and the obstacles it faces. I attended a key kick-off meeting with a safety professional who didn't seem his usual enthusiastic self. I'll call him Ian Morgan. As we chatted away, waiting for the board to join us (they were late), he explained that he was having a bad day. A very bad day, actually, as he explained that he'd just buried his father that morning. I was staggered, and asked, 'What on earth are you doing here?!' He simply said, 'Because this session is really important . . . they just haven't *got it* yet'.

I found this really humbling, and it reminded me that whilst the *devil* can certainly be in the detail of a simple conversation or act, so too can *inspiration*. Ian Whittingham, MBE, used to describe the aftermath of the fall that paralysed him to remind us that the impact of events ripple out, like dropping a stone in a pond. This works for positive events too. When I feel I'm banging my head against a wall of 'impressive words, less impressive action', I think of Ian Morgan and the others like him I've been lucky enough to meet. As the philosopher Edmund Burke said:

> *There is no greater mistake than for a man than to do nothing at all because he can only do a little.*

In a later chapter, we'll discuss the fact that 'good work is good for you', and that people who enjoy their work tend to be psychologically healthier than those that don't need to work at all. (The reverse is also true, of course.) An enriching and supportive work culture makes peoples' lives better; a blame-filled toxic one makes their lives worse. This book addresses what 'good' looks like in day-to-day terms.

I used to say, 'Every single good safety conversation sends out positive ripples, as Ian described, and is a brick in the wall of a strong safety culture'. I should have been saying more simply that every good conversation sends out positive ripples, and is a brick in the wall of a supportive culture generally. Nothing is more important and far-reaching than good dialogue.

Tim Marsh, February 2021

Section one

A little theory

CHAPTER 1

Why bother?

In this chapter I will cover:

- The limitations of compliance.
- The vital importance of day-to-day behaviour.
- Why you can't change behaviour with exhortations to 'have a good attitude' in the medium-to-long term.
- The vital importance of Heinrich's Principle and how it relates to wellbeing, mental health, safety, and pretty much everything else.
  - Where mental health and general wellbeing overlap and interlink with physical safety.

Why bother?

Especially if you've been *given* this book to read, you may be asking 'why do we need this?' After all, the company has some lovely certificates on the reception wall that are clear proof that you've passed some impressive-sounding safety and health audits. Maybe you can't even recall the last serious accident. And as for mental health, well, one of the certificates shows the company has trained up a whole bunch of mental health first aiders. (We'll be returning frequently to the importance and hidden costs of the mental health issue.)

On the other hand, even if your organisation is broadly compliant, there's a good chance that although accident rates are at their best-ever levels historically, they've plateaued over the past few years. More than that, they may well not be anywhere near best in class (as is a key strategic aim), and senior management are determined that they *will* improve.

Sometimes this is the consequence of a serious incident, and sometimes because senior management have been proactively

DOI: 10.4324/9781003177784-3

convinced that good safety and health is good business – as in, 'if you think safety is expensive, try having an accident' – or maybe the company has been bought by a parent organisation with a more stringent mindset towards such issues.

Leaving aside the moral argument, the new owners may be very aware that excellent safety also has the spin-off benefits of enhanced reputation, improved morale, and minimised disruption. More than that, getting to truly world-class safety performance *inevitably* requires the embedding of a set of generic day-to-day behaviours whose effectiveness will generalise to everything, from quality through morale to productivity. It also generalises to mental health and wellbeing because, as we'll see, 'good work is good for you'.

Around a decade ago, Ryder-Marsh staff came up with an adaptation of the classic Parker and Hudson culture model that always resonates wherever it is presented around the world. It suggests that many organisations reach their best-ever levels through compliance, but then try to improve further with more of the same, despite diminishing returns really kicking in. They end up spinning in circles of paper and process. Instead, we suggested a step change in mentality towards a humanistic, holistic, and genuinely person-centred approach.

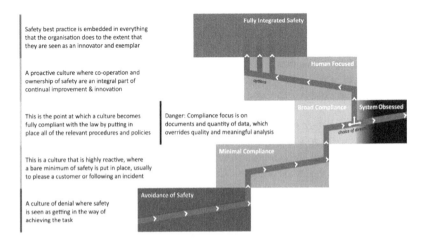

Figure 1.1 Safety culture development model (Ryder-Marsh Safety)

At first, we talked, as above, about developing a pro-active safety culture with many meaningful spinoff benefits for other fields. It becomes more and more apparent we should have been talking about developing a person-centred, proactive culture, with one of the meaningful spinoff benefits being safety.

Increasingly, organisations are seeking excellence in the field of mental health and wellbeing for their own sake. Traditionally, it's not something we've been very good at in the UK, but we have been world class at safety for many decades and there are many proven methodologies that directly translate. This experience highlights how many organisations are making the same mistake with their wellbeing and mental health initiatives that they made with behavioural safety decades ago. (This book could be subtitled, 'Focusing only on the symptoms, not the root cause, didn't work then for behavioural safety, never was going to work – so it won't work now for mental health'.)

As above, genuine excellence requires far more than good systems. It also requires an ongoing, day-to-day commitment to intelligent analysis, constructive communication, and empowerment. No organisation that genuinely embeds these as part of 'the way we do things around here' can possibly fail to derive all sorts of spinoff benefits, which include mental health and wellbeing.

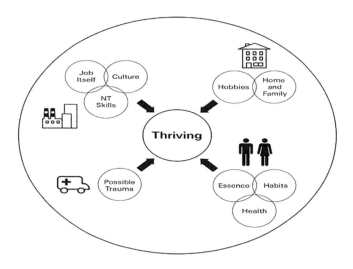

Figure 1.2 Thriving

This model (Figure 1.2) of thriving was included in a Campbell Institute white paper on the future of wellbeing, and stresses the overlapping and interconnected nature of things at work. We all know that people 'are who they are', but it's also true that we are what we do more than what we say we do, and good habits can be developed over time. More than that, recent studies show that we can change, as people, far more than we traditionally thought we could, and, crucially, that organisations can facilitate and 'nudge' these positive changes. These changes can then impact the quality of our family life and relationships, and virtuous circles are set up.

We know that culture is king, and that day to day, it manifests itself most obviously in the interactions between supervisors and employees. Nearly all organisations claim that 'our people are our greatest asset', but this doesn't stop many of them running a short-term, blame-driven toxic culture as they do. Only the psychotic actually thrive in such cultures – most merely do their best to survive. And as Maya Angelou so memorably put it:

> It is not about surviving, it is about thriving, with passion, compassion, humour and style.

THE LIMITATIONS OF COMPLIANCE

Many organisations reach a level of systems compliance that will please an auditing body and, as above, lead to lots of nice certificates in the lobby. These are, of course, very reassuring at a glance. (Though to be honest, no senior person in the safety culture field pays much attention at all to the certificates and awards in the foyer that the various auditing organisations deliver. At least, not unless they aren't there *at all*, of course!)

However, the observation that out in the field 'compliance is *discretionary*' is absolutely true, and underpins much of the rationale behind this book. More importantly, basic compliance simply isn't sufficient if you want to achieve any sort of *excellence*, because research suggests that there is a better correlation between, for example, workforce *involvement* in safety and incident rate, than *compliance* and incident rate. As we will see, genuine involvement in safety and health correlates well with genuine involvement generally, which itself correlates with any definition of 'good work'.

This is not to downplay the vital underpinning importance of robust and efficient systems, but please consider this question. Would you prefer your ten-year-old to simply step into the road blindly at a level crossing because the green 'walk' sign has come on, or would you prefer them to cross 50 yards down the road whilst at the same time 'dynamic risk assessing' effectively as they do?

Companies like Premier Foods are aware of this, and have recently been running much-lauded and award-winning safety campaigns, where the emphasis is on fewer but *better* rules that are easier to enforce consistently and fairly. They are actively seeking to get away from compliance as an 'end in itself', and promote more *thinking* and *empowerment* around risk in a search for genuine excellence. More than that, increased fairness and consistency leads to more trust. The UK's leading stress guru of the last 30 years, Sir Cary Cooper, has constantly said that 'degree of trust' should be an organisation's number one metric. (I disagree, but only to push for quality of dialogue and analysis as even more important because of their role in *developing* trust).

What this means is that even if our employees actually do follow all the rules, we are still likely to be some way short of excellence. That's of course hypothetical, because they *don't* always follow the rules. Recently the expressions 'operational discipline' and 'operating dexterity' have become much in vogue. What they mean, in simple terms, is thinking intelligently, imaginatively, and flexibly around a solid foundation of controls.

It should all start with a focus on everyday behaviour.

THE VITAL IMPORTANCE OF BEHAVIOUR

There are two reasons why a behavioural focus is vital.

UNSAFE DAY-TO-DAY BEHAVIOUR CORRELATES WITH LOSS

There is always a direct link between the number of unsafe or unhealthy acts and the number of accidents and illnesses. From the safety world, Heinrich's original triangle (see Figure 1.3) suggested that there are, on average, 300 unsafe acts per accident, and the most recent HSE figures suggest two million unsafe behaviours per fatality. Arguing over the *exact* levels in the ratio doesn't matter, as it changes from time to time and in place to place. The simple fact is that there *is* a ratio. On balance, we hurt many more people than we kill, and we usually get away with a wide range of unsafe behaviours. Likewise, lots of people undertake lots of unhealthy acts and don't even suffer consequences in the long term. (We all know someone who smoked 40 cigarettes a day and lived to die of old age.) In similar vein, many people work in toxic thankless cultures without suffering a breakdown. Millions of people, in fact.

But not all. (Figures suggest that somewhere between 20 and 30 per cent of working people are 'struggling', and that was before Covid-19.)

For example, if the true likelihood of falling down the stairs of a building is 100,000 to one, but one million people use the stairs annually – with none of them holding the handrail – then you'll have ten accidents a year (give or take). If 90 per cent comply, then there would be only one accident a year on average, but if we can get 99 per cent to comply, then there would be only one accident every ten years or so – and 'zero accidents' becomes a possibility.

It's a simple numbers game.

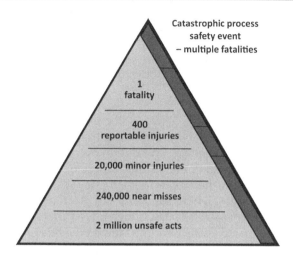

Catastrophic process
safety event
– multiple fatalities

1
fatality

400
reportable injuries

20,000 minor injuries

240,000 near misses

2 million unsafe acts

Figure 1.3 Occupational and process safety

Source: Adapted from H.W. Heinrich, 1959.

Notes: Attempts to show different triangles for process safety and personal safety suggest that the two are separate. Treating them as such is highly likely to be unproductive, as several infamous case studies have shown. Although the outcomes can be different (EG injury on the one hand, loss of containment on the other), and the potential severity greater with an outright process failure, they are often different symptoms of the same root causes.

Case study. Management visiting Deepwater Horizon infamously asked about personal safety, but not about process safety issues like 'kicks' from wells that really should have raised red flags. This shouldn't be an either/or situation where 'behavioural safety distracted'; this merely reflected BP's ongoing problems with process safety. (See, for example, Texas City.) They merely convinced themselves they were (now) good at safety *generally* because they'd become good at personal safety. They were wrong. I think that infamous comment 'I want my life back' implied a certain lack of patience, and that certain lack of patience possibly pointing at the true value base.

HEINRICH'S PRINCIPLE AND GRAVITY

This principle is important, since for most companies, the majority of accidents will be the result of simple slips, trips, falls, and 'struck by's, so although excellent process safety is of course utterly vital to ensure something catastrophic doesn't happen, it's virtually impossible to have world-class safety figures without a behavioural approach. (An illustration: there have been more fatalities offshore caused by falls than in all the process safety incidents combined – Piper Alpha included.)

The staircase example above is illustrative, as the majority of accidents have gravity as the root cause, and however sophisticated our systems, we can't design out gravity if we want to move our product or our people. (Think of any famous people who've been in the media following an accident. It's difficult to find any at all where the word 'fall' isn't involved: from the tragic death of actress Natasha Richardson after a fall on a nursery ski slope, to Ozzie Osborne falling off a quad bike, to Keith Richards falling from a coconut tree. Even the great Michael Schumacher, having survived the world of Formula One, suffered life-changing injuries while skiing.)

Even call centre employees will have to climb stairs, and for many giant utility companies, the single biggest cause of accidents is retail staff tripping over in the street walking from house to house and trying to update their palmtops as they go. Two interesting facts: one, about ten times as many people are killed each year by falling coconuts as by sharks, with the numbers usually around 20:200. Two, more people were killed erecting wind farms prior to 2013 than by all nuclear accidents ever. (Terrifying though that superb series 'Chernobyl' was.)

Because unsafe behaviours very rarely result in a near miss (let alone anything more serious), it's easy to assume they never will, and forget Heinrich's Principle. But here's a simple example to bear in mind: the first sunny weekend in spring in the UK will see lots of children bouncing around on trampolines all day, and many of them will be unguarded. By the end of the day, *inevitably*, a handful will have suffered what are called 'life-changing' injuries. Hospital A&E departments know this well, but no one can tell you the children's names yet.

It's a simple numbers game: the bigger the number at the bottom of the triangle, the bigger the number at the top will be. More positively, the opposite is also true. The smaller the number at the bottom of the triangle, the smaller the top number will be. This time, of course, we'll *never* know the names of those saved. Replace a kick board that stops an accidently kicked scaffold clip from falling, and the person below with their hard hat in their hand and in the line of fire won't even know that they just used one of their nine lives. (If it's the hard hat that breaks the chain, then they'll certainly know all about it – but they'll survive. Got that t-shirt!).

The vast majority of fatalities are caused not by genuinely dangerous things, but by moderately dangerous things we've done thousands of times before – but which cross-reference with distraction, over-confidence, or anger. The same is true of health. We don't die of heart attacks because we ate a double burger and chips and followed it with a cigarette, but because the first 10,000 we ate and smoked didn't kill us, so we assumed they never would and carried on.

BEHAVIOUR SETS THE TONE AND IS SELF-REINFORCING

The second reason is that the very best definition of safety culture is 'the way we typically do things around here'. As in all walks of life, a handful of key behaviours will set the tone, and the first thing that we do in a new situation is to look about and 'check out what's what'. If we see half the 'regulars' acting safely and half unsafely, then as a new starter or subcontractor, we can do pretty much what we want and not stand out. However, if we can improve these key behaviours so that 90 per cent comply (the fabled 'tipping point'), then these behaviours become self-sustaining.

These key behaviours will range from the simple 'hold the handrail', 'look where you're walking', and 'using PPE', as mentioned previously, through to the quality of a toolbox talk, or the number of structured or unstructured (but quality) dialogues about safety, health, or wellbeing. Or perhaps there's an MD who closes out a strategy meeting that discusses cost-cutting with an aggressive, 'Any problems with that!? No? Good! Get on with it then'. (And we're back to BP and their former, very ambitious, boss. It's reported that Texas City were much in favour initially because they didn't push back on cuts as much as others.)

BEHAVIOUR AND PEER PRESSURE

The latest studies suggest that 80 per cent of what we learn is from our peers – only 5 per cent from formal training.

Imagine arriving in a new country and being told by the hire car people, 'We're brutal with speeding on this island; don't even think about exceeding 100 kph'; reinforced with huge threatening signs as you drive out of the airport. You'd very probably join the motorway at 95kph. Then you find in practice that the inside lane is averaging 110, the middle 120, and the outside lane is a complete free-for-all. What speed would you be doing five minutes later? (At conferences, people would always say, 'Well, you have to keep up with flow for safety', so I started asking, 'How many of us would have used the *outside lane* within half an hour?' Interestingly, it's always about 50 per cent!)

Vision statements and company values are of course vital in setting the tone, but they are the very definition of 'necessary but not *sufficient*'. They (should!) certainly *influence* the culture, but they are not *it*. The day-to-day behaviour is the culture – and it is almost impossible to overstate its importance.

YOU CAN'T ADDRESS BEHAVIOUR BY EXHORTING 'HAVE A GOOD ATTITUDE!'

Just about every study shows that 50 per cent of us think we have an average attitude, and 50 per cent a *good* attitude (I exaggerate, but only a little – the actual figures from a famous Scottish driving study are about 48 per cent and 49 per cent). So, when we talk about people who cut corners and take risks and say, 'You know who you are!', the entire audience will point to the person next to them, saying 'I hope you're listening – they're talking about *you*'. We all know people with a poor attitude, of course, but it's almost never the person in the mirror. And because there's nothing wrong with our attitudes, *thank you very much*, we don't need to change them. I mean, have you ever won an argument about sport, politics, or religion? Ever?

Inspirational speakers can help get through this denial in the *short term*, just as new football managers can induce a sudden boost in performance, during the 'honeymoon period'. After listening to an inspirational speaker who is, perhaps, talking from a wheelchair after being paralysed in a fall, we may find ourselves thinking, 'Yes, that really *could* be me', and vow to make a greater effort to cut fewer corners. However, this honeymoon period hardly ever lasts, and soon enough we are back to the old habits. In the wellbeing field, for example, we know that dieting simply doesn't work. Indeed, we can confuse our bodies' physiology with a diet and put more weight on when we go back to old habits. If we want to lose weight and *keep it off*, we need to make *indefinite* lifestyle changes.

To improve medium-to-long term, we need to *change* something. (In football terms, it might be cleverly re-organising the team, signing the missing piece of the jigsaw puzzle like an Eric Cantona or a Virgil Van Dyke, better organisation at set pieces, or improving fitness levels.) In safety and health terms, we need to change the working environment, or else the maxim 'if you do what you always did, you get what you always got' soon applies.

A first discussion of mental health first aiders should be made here, as there's a similarity here with inspirational speakers. Yes, they can be of great benefit and can symbolise management commitment. But if what they most symbolise is a tickbox/'magic bullet' approach, then nothing much will change in the medium-to-long term. If the work environment is hugely pressured, blame-riddled, and toxic, resources are limited, and management think Dale Carnegie used to play full back for West Ham or wide receiver for the Dallas Cowboys, then the stress that comes with that will deliver 'bad work is bad for you'. Talking about it helps – talking always helps – but not as much as dealing with the root cause.

BUT IF THEY JUST TOOK MORE CARE!

An average person, fit, rested, and stress-free, can only concentrate around 55 minutes an hour. If you're tired, stressed about relationships or money worries, 'struggling' with a mental health issue, or 'jet-lagged' coming off a split shift, it's worse. If you have a workforce of 20,000, that's 16,000 hours a week of away-with-the-fairies zombie time. And that's the *absolute minimum*.

So, by the laws of nature, 'take care at all times' simply can't work. However, if we acknowledge this and, for example, get into the good habit of tidying up poor housekeeping when we are bright and alert, then that trip hazard isn't there when we come back around the corner away with the fairies ten minutes later.

Away with the fairies/
in need of a re-charge

BAD DAY

Alert, focused and productive

Figure 1.4 Amount of time struggling – on a good day

We've used these pie graphics to illustrate the issue. Reflecting the above, Human Error Golden Rule number one from James Reason is that even the best people make mistakes. The rest of the rules essentially say that these mistakes typically cluster, and we must systemically understand why these clusters occur, so we can get in front of them and proactively mitigate the impact, if not design them out. Exactly.

He also says we should strive to make good people great, but I (humbly) suggest he was looking in the wrong direction here, even before the challenges of 'long Covid' came along to make matters worse. Because for many people, the bigger blue pie applies on many days, and I think our major focus really should be on keeping average people upright.

Figure 1.5 Amount of time struggling – on a bad day

I want to suggest that the causes of this larger pie are many, varied, and usually intricately interlinked. Importantly, though many are individual, some are organisational and can be made better or worse by organisational experiences. Understand how bad things are, and why they are, and then halving the problem *for the average worker* will utterly transform any organisational culture.

Fatigue

This is a huge area, but to summarise the key issues here: **tired** people have exactly the same physiology as drunk people. They are low in resilience, can be impetuous, low in focus, slow in reaction, and prone to physical and emotional clumsiness. In short, tired people have *big* blue pies!

We all know that 'nothing beats a good night's sleep', that in evolutionary terms the light bulb has been around for seconds, and that all our nan's advice about sleep ('early to bed . . .') was actually on the money, but there are lots of excellent best-selling books covering this topic in depth, so I'll leave it there. Suffice to say that there has been a massive increase in appreciation in recent years that when it comes to safety and health, it's very difficult to overstate the importance of your fatigue monitoring and management process.

Focus, incidents, and mental health

This is perhaps the core of the book: the growing appreciation that 'struggling' workers have big blue pies too.

Whether caused by the illness itself, the medication taken to control the illness, or by lifestyle issues such as self-medication, which are notoriously difficult to untangle, three behavioural issues seem to be central to a link between mental health and A&E (see HSE RR 488):

1   A lack of focus and situational awareness – more likely to be oblivious to risk.
2   An increased fatalism and disengagement – less likely to care about risk.

3   An increased impetuosity and lack of control – more likely
     to actively create risk.

(We work with an insurance company that likes using three-letter acronyms to make things memorable for clients, and they use WWF – as in 'what?', '*whatever*', and 'f*** it'.)

It's not as simple as saying depressed people are more likely to be fatalistic and anxious people more likely to be distracted, because, for example, anxious people can be hypervigilant. (Though often they are hypervigilant about issues to which they give too much importance – distracting them from the real risk.) Regardless, though conclusive data is hard to come by, an Australian study of 60,000 workers sounds credible. It suggests that incidents increase by between 50 and 150 per cent, depending on the situation and the severity of the issues being faced, and that individuals are only 70 per cent as likely to contribute to 'successful' behaviour. The authors don't define what they mean by success, but this book does when it talks about 'culture creation' and how that manifests on a day-to-day basis.

Wellbeing and mental health

When employees are just going through the motions and are disengaged, it costs organisations lots of money, but disengaged employees are not just more likely to be accident prone, they are also not getting the benefit of 'good work is good for you'. Some really struggle, become utterly miserable, and are just existing.

For some it's worse than that, and you might be surprised to know that, as mentioned in the introduction, the ratio of work-place fatalities to working-age suicides is 31 to 1 in the UK. (It's less in countries with accident rates that aren't as good as the UK's, but it's always striking.) Wherever you are reading this, the bottom of this particular triangle is huge, and doesn't manifest itself in slips and bumps that can be measured. It manifests itself primarily in absenteeism, turnover, presenteeism, lack of engagement, poor relationships, and the day-to-day issues around self-neglect and self-medication.

Figure 1.6 A simple summary of the majority of day to day mental health issues faced by people in work

We've found that this simple cartoon helps explain 'mental health' in ways any organisation can understand. The first thing to note is that the issues it covers cause around 85 per cent of the trillions of dollars lost to MH annually around the world. (The other 15 per cent relate to issues such as schizophrenia, psychosis, hormonal issues like post-natal depression, and PTSD). In the US alone, the issues in this simplistic depression and/or anxiety cartoon are estimated to cost the economy two trillion dollars annually. (So, the classic '*whatever it is* at the moment, *halve it*' step change would be worth a round trillion.)

We nearly all have the thoughts and emotions in the cartoon, but some people have so many of them it reaches critical levels. A cognitive behaviour therapist would say that every minute spent wishing something hadn't happened is a minute wasted, as it simply isn't going to unhappen. (Learning from and motivation to learn aside, of course.) Likewise, every minute worrying that something that hasn't happened yet *will* happen steals a minute from us that could be spent working to ensure it doesn't. This is of course very much aligned with mindfully being in the moment, and simple but profound sayings such as:

> *Give me the serenity to deal with the things I cannot change, the strength to deal with those I can, and the wisdom to know the difference.*

Almost everyone reading this book will already know how we should seek to address these issues at the source. We should strive to eat well, sleep well, drink in moderation, exercise, meditate, invest time in our relationships and work-life balance, and keep a daily gratitude diary – indeed, all the things we see in the newspapers every day about how to mitigate the effects of 'long Covid'.

Organisations

I think organisations, in the simplest terms, just need to strive for two things *strategically*. (We'll discuss 'bikes and bananas' *initiatives* later.) The first is to be mindful that inevitably a significant percentage of their staff will be teetering on the edge of critical. A 'culture of care' delivered through systems such as the 'walk and talk' will help ensure staff know 'it's OK to not be OK'. This will help us spot people in time, and point them at Occupational Health and Employee Assistance. (Note that mental health first aiders can help here too, but are not essential if *everyone* is contributing.)

The second, more proactive, approach is to strive to create a strong, genuinely caring, empowering, and supportive culture that naturally helps keep employees mentally strong through the benefits of 'good work is good for you'.

Putting free fruit in reception helps. Subsidised gym membership and on-site meditation classes help (though both will be most utilised by employees who already eat fruit and work out as part of a daily routine!). Health campaigns with charity prizes for the team that takes most steps help. Sleep workshops help. Free blackout materials for shift workers help too. However, we're just not going to make much of a dent in the bottom of the overall well-being triangle with 'bikes and bananas' schemes, because most of the stresses in work are psycho-social and about the job itself, the way it's organised, and the people we interact with as we do.

No one ever said of Munch's painting *The Scream*, 'What that poor man needs is a nice banana'.

Let's examine 'good' and 'bad' work in more detail.

Warr's Vitamin Model provides an excellent framework for considering what might make a job rewarding and engaging for a given *individual*. It's a *vitamin* model; as Warr stresses, there may be too little or too much of any given item, and these will differ from person to person. We know, for example, that some people thrived working from home during the Covid-19 crisis, and others hated it. (Having partners and children at home are a factor that works both ways – sometimes for the same person on the same day!)

Warr's elements

Money and physical security: Many studies have shown that 'enough' money is all you need for psychological health. One thing is for certain, though – nearly all organisations report that any money management workshops offered to staff have more attendees than they were expecting, and feedback afterwards suggests that more people found them really useful than they expected. In terms of physical security, most of us like a certain degree of physical comfort, but others rather like working in the wind and the rain! Risk appetites differ greatly, too.

Goal and task demands (& uncertainty): Most of us like a quite hard, clearly defined goal, please! (Some like a real challenge, and others a very gentle challenge, but we nearly all hate ambiguity! The same is true of **uncertainty** – just watch travellers at an airport who have been told nothing but 'flight delayed').

Opportunity for control. Some hate to be told what to do by anyone, ever. Others find a lack of structure very stressful.

Opportunity for skill use and variety. Some people really, *really* love variety and the chance to develop and use new skills. Others are more comfortable with routine and repetition.

Valued social position. None of us want to feel undervalued, but again, it's a very personal thing. A McJob may well be seen very differently by different people. Consider someone who's just secured a degree in a prestigious subject and, for example, wants to be a human rights lawyer, but has 'only' managed to secure a 'McJob'. Then consider someone who has just arrived as an immigrant from a poor and war-ravaged country and who is just thrilled to be employed at all, so they stride from the house each morning thinking, 'A job! A real paying job with benefits, and with one of the world's most famous companies, too!' Likewise, you may wonder why so many excellent hotel staff in the UK are Eastern European. I'm assured it's because hospitality is traditionally considered a valued and prestigious job there.

Interpersonal contact: I have saved perhaps the most important till last. Some people are quite solitary and find teamwork stressful. Others are gregarious and find solitude excruciating. But all agree that colleagues lacking in social skills and emotional intelligence are a bloody nightmare, especially if they are your manager or supervisor, and they need to talk to you about the items above – so that they can tweak them to maximise your job satisfaction and engagement, hence ensuring you find your working day as rewarding and motivating as you might like. Or not. (You're with me on this one, I imagine!)

DEATH BY A THOUSAND CUTS

In recent years, there has been an increase in the number of organisations looking proactively at 'psychological safety'. Previously, even in occupations where the risk of trauma was obvious (IE, frontline news reporting, frontline services, and forces), the approach was to wait for people to burn out or implode, and then give them time off to regroup and recover. (You've seen the films, I'm sure.) In recent times, organisations like TikTok and Facebook have head-hunted experienced people from such organisations to run systemic risk-based approaches – essentially employing the same 'assess, design out, mitigate' methodologies you would use to minimise harm from chemicals. (For example, content moderators need to check if material is unacceptable, so they do need to view it, but they don't necessarily need the added trauma of hearing it, too.)

The point is that the vast majority of working people who take their own lives, suffer breakdowns, or are merely 'hanging by a thread' are not the result of seeing the after-effects of a bomb in a marketplace or images of abuse. They have instead suffered 'death by a thousand cuts'.

WELLBEING: MEANING (AND RESILIENCE)

To put this in context, there are many holistic wellbeing models that broadly cover the same areas. One of the best-known models considers five factors:

1 Financial security (enough money).
2 Good work (both as above).
3 Relationships with family and friends.
4 Emotional and physical health (of course).
5 Contributing.

This latter one can be thought of as 'being useful', having meaning, traction – the stuff we do that makes us feel we are paying into the humanity bank, and not just withdrawing from it. The why we get out of bed. This may well be voluntary work or family-oriented work, but for many, it's their *job*.

To slightly paraphrase John Lennon in *The End* (the final track on *Abbey Road*), 'In the end, the care we get is equal to the care we give'. Genuinely being someone who pays in more than they take out really helps our state of mind. Organisations should always be mindful that this is the case, and also be mindful of the effects where no such opportunities exist.

In one of the best-selling books of all time on this subject, *Man's Search for Meaning*, Viktor Frankl (the leading psychologist and Auschwitz survivor) makes the case that with a strong 'why', we can overcome almost any 'what'. In his own case, this was to survive the death camp so he could rewrite the manuscript of a book he was just finishing and took with him to 'work on whilst in prison'.

For some, our work gives us meaning in life. For others, it provides the funds to do the things we find meaningful, and for most, it's some combination of the two. (For some lost souls, money is an end in and of itself – but that's OK, since a good 'walk and talk' delivers a 'win-win', so they'll be happy too).

But the key point is that it's a very personal thing, and we need to talk to people to understand their reality. The classic example is the person who loves to work on practical matters in a team and for whom promotion to a management role proves, in time, to be the worst day of their lives. (This isn't the place to talk about training, mentoring and ongoing support.) A more positive example is the famous story of the caretaker approached by President Kennedy when sweeping up one day at NASA. His reply to the question, 'What're you doing today?' could, I always think, have started with, 'Well, WTF does it look like . . .', but instead was, 'Helping put a man on the moon, Mr President'.

I'd like to check his body language and voice tone to be sure (85% of communication being dependent upon those), but that aside, there's a man who has already answered the question, 'How are you?' – well, for that day, at least.

GOOD HABITS: THEIR ADOPTION AND THEIR FACILITATION

On training courses, I've often used some real-life CCTV footage of a young man being knocked off a motorbike by a driver undertaking an illegal U-turn to escape a traffic jam. The motorcyclist is compliant, as he wasn't speeding and had every right to be using the outside lane. However, he wasn't driving proactively. (Proactive driving principles are those such as 'always give yourself the time and space to deal with the mistakes of others as well as your own', and 'assume everyone else is a drunken idiot'.)

I once showed this film to some managers when team training with an ex elite special-forces soldier who was waiting to teach them defensive driving techniques. He said something very interesting:

> You all know me as someone very risk tolerant, and if you saw me riding my motorbike in the woods on a weekend, you'd be mortified. But this simply wouldn't have happened to me, because though I'm very risk tolerant, I'm also very risk aware. I'd have noticed the curve in the road reducing visibility, I'd have noticed all those frustrated drivers, and I'd have noticed that there was no barrier separating them from me – and without thinking about it, I'd have moved to the inside lane to give myself some space.

27

Often, when we're tired and distracted, the *only* thing that *can* save us are our good habits. And, as above, this is where the overlap with wellbeing and mental health is very explicit. Tired people have more accidents. People who are disengaged and lacking energy and/or pre-occupied with personal worries have more accidents. People who are angry at the way they've been treated or who have become fatalistic have more accidents.

Creating a culture of care: the aforementioned tired, disengaged, and/or angry people are also far more likely to walk past an opportunity to build a safe and healthy culture of genuine care, but habits can help here. Have you ever been told, 'You're a really nice person and I really like you, but . . .' and had that sentence end well?! This is because we always put the important part of the message after the 'but', so we all know that when a sentence starts well but then contains a 'but', there's a problem coming. When told, 'This job needs doing safely, *but* by Friday', both parties may be unaware of how the real message was communicated – but communicated it is, as you'll almost certainly get the job by Friday as safely as is viable. However, this mindset technique can also *help* in any number of ways. For example, changing the habit of thinking, 'They are normally OK, but today they are really annoying me' – which points at frustration and conflict – and instead training yourself to think, 'They are really annoying me, but they are normally OK', will point you towards empathy and analysis.

Likewise, getting into the habit of asking, 'What do you need from me?' or 'Are you OK?' really helps on those days when energy levels are low, and it's 'you, but on a *bad* day' (to reverse the advert).

HEINRICH, PROCESS SAFETY, SUSTAINABILITY, AND GENERIC LEARNING

It's worth acknowledging that the Heinrich ratios do vary depending on the behaviours in question and the potential outcomes. Some of these behaviours are frequent and low in potential (though note that, as above, even trips on flat surfaces cause multiple fatalities every year).

Others are less frequent but more likely to cause fatalities – a steeper triangle, if you like. This, of course, is especially true when we look at process safety issues.

However, the two things aren't separate, but interlink and overlap. A good example of an overlap would be the housekeeping on the Piper Alpha oil platform, which was notoriously poor. (Piper Alpha was the North Sea oil platform that exploded in 1988, causing the loss of 167 lives.)

Any meaningful analysis of the poor housekeeping before the accident would have taken the auditor straight to the permit-to-work system. (The permit-to-work system weakness was perhaps considered *the* key cause of the explosion.) The permits contained a 'housekeeping right?' element which, in light of the poor housekeeping, would have clearly demonstrated a tick-box mentality lacking control. Obviously, this would have been a very useful issue to have picked up on and addressed in early 1988.

Indeed, much unsafe behaviour will be caused in large part by complex organisational weaknesses around communication, ergonomics, staffing, and resources that can have devastating organisational consequences.

Therefore, although the dedicated safety and health conversation that this book covers can never take the place of effective and interlinked systems, monitoring and auditing, it certainly should *complement* them. A good conversation really should often seek to directly *address* these in-depth issues when possible. Even when it doesn't directly address them, an intelligent, open conversation –even about something as 'relatively trivial' as housekeeping, PPE compliance, a cancelled training course, or anything at all genuinely considered 'unfair' in the canteen – could very well lead to an underlying cause that could be instrumental in causing something catastrophic.

In the world of safety, the catastrophe makes the front pages, as does an outage that closes a major airport. In the world of sustainability, it tends to make the business pages in a few years – when so many individuals have suffered 'death by a thousand cuts', the organisation itself does too.

SUMMARY OF KEY POINTS

To reiterate, organisational excellence is about cultural excellence, which is in large part about day-to-day *behavioural* excellence. The next few chapters discuss leadership excellence. This book is specifically about safety and health leadership, but before we get to the safety and health conversation itself, let me introduce leadership more generally.

CHAPTER 2

Safety and health excellence (is just excellence)

In this chapter, I will cover:

- Strategic high-level safety and health (briefly).
- The principles behind devoting time to a 'walk and talk'.
- The opportunity a 'walk and talk' gives to genuinely 'lead', the way the inspirational speakers say we should.
- The output of transformational leadership.
- Two new and hugely influential concepts, one general and one safety-and-health-specific which help put theory I've covered into context.
- A good old-fashioned checklist of suggested issues to look out for – during a 'walk and talk', or at any time.

STRATEGIC SAFETY

It's been said, 'You get the safety levels senior management want – all else is just detail and case study'. The same is true of wellbeing. Words are nice, but the organisation will be, by definition, perfectly resourced and organised to deliver what it's currently delivering.

One of our clients is considered very much the health and safety leader in their field. This stems from an incident at a funeral some 11 years ago, when they were very average in terms of safety standards. An employee had been killed, and at the funeral, a rather apprehensive MD was approached by the widow, who, instead of attacking or abusing him (as he expected), thanked him sincerely for showing her husband the respect of attending. Relieved and humbled, he made himself a promise.

DOI: 10.4324/9781003177784-4

Obviously, this book cannot be of much use where there is little high-level commitment to improve. Excellent safety and health management at a *strategic* level is always essential. Two other examples of that: we have a client that bought into an industry (waste disposal), but found in practice that because of historical contracts, the promise 'safely or not at all' simply couldn't be kept if a profit was to be made. They stuck to their values and exited. Another client, in the offshore oil and gas industry, has a rule that although they will (for any number of realistic commercial reasons) subcontract a high-risk activity, they will only subcontract it *once*. The company they contract has to undertake *all* activities, as they know that each time an activity is contracted, a little more control is lost and a little more risk and variability added. (How nice for them to have the best of both worlds! But then, it's always been true that he who pays the piper . . .)

These examples reflect a genuinely high level of commitment to safety excellence, and organisations like this will often benchmark themselves against acknowledged industry leaders. Nothing can replace this, but a good 'walk and talk' can remind an organisation that things are never as good as assumed. (And it's a great truism that if we're not pushing forwards, then we're almost certainly drifting back to the norm.) In recent years, the expression 'there's safety as *said* and safety as *done*' has been popularised by the Safety Differently movement. Every time I've heard it used, *everyone* knows exactly what it means!

These hard-won truisms apply equally to mental health and wellbeing. Just because there's not a queue of people threatening to throw themselves from the roof doesn't mean that 'our greatest assets' are all thriving. We need to commit to proactively monitoring them and striving to ensure they are.

WHERE A 'WALK AND TALK' FITS IN: WE MUST DEVOTE THE TIME TO SHOW LEADERSHIP VISIBLY

First, the 'walk and talk' simply gives a practical demonstration that safety and wellbeing is indeed as important as it's claimed to be in the values statements and visions that a company has. (We believe all accidents are preventable, we have a culture of care, our people are our biggest asset, and so on.) The 'walk and talk' shows *'visible* felt leadership', as it is sometimes known. It's simple: if you are seen to be actively devoting time to it, the workforce is more likely to believe you really mean it.

I do feel that less than one dedicated half-hour walk in a week really isn't enough to achieve this 'visibility'. (Some senior people in the field, like the much-vaunted consultant Peter McKie, recommend at least 30 minutes a *day* – with the quip that it 'still leaves 7 ½ hours to do the less important things', and to question why they don't have 30 minutes a day to address their 'number one priority'.)

There has been universal agreement recently that 'talking' about mental health issues is key, as in, 'It's OK to not be OK'. Again, it's worth stressing that if all supervisors and colleagues got into the habit of asking, 'And how are *you*?', as recommended in Section Two, then, I'd argue, formal mental health first aiders would be largely superfluous.

LOOK ACTIVELY FOR THE HOLES IN THE SYSTEM, BECAUSE THEY ARE ALWAYS THERE!

Let's assume that your company has broadly reached compliance in its systems and procedures. It has good training, robust induction and risk assessment processes, and up-to-date safety management systems. However, like all companies, what it says in the file and what happens in practice are not always the same, and the inevitable 'holes in the system' need investigating and plugging. This is particularly so given most companies' constant need to change and update. (The essence of Andrew Hopkin's hugely influential 'mindful' culture model is that there will always be something not going as planned – or about to not go as planned – and the weak organisations let these issues find them. The better, proactive organisations seek these issues out.)

This applies equally to wellbeing. In previous chapters, we've stressed that in any typical organisation, a meaningful percentage of employees will be struggling with anxiety and/or depression, or worse. (Increasingly, we're seeing companies around the world, previously in denial, forced to address high-pressure and bullying norms only when there's a *cluster of suicides*.)

The key thing in proven best practise is not to let the problems find us – we must go out and proactively find them. There is a very well-known '(fail to) spot a big gorilla amidst mingling basketball players' clip. What it illustrates, of course, is the point that if you walk the site looking *only* for safety and health issues, you'll not see a *little* more, you'll see ten times as much as if you look for safety and health issues whilst going about your day job. (In the exercise, the 'day job' is represented by counting passes between fast-mingling players.)

WE BEST LEARN WHY OUR PEOPLE DO WHAT THEY DO FROM TALKING TO THEM

The third reason for the 'walk and talk' strand is Elvis' 'walk a mile in a man's shoes' rule, crossed with Reason's 'just culture' model and his 'even the best people make mistakes' assertion as well as Dekker's 'new view' of human error. (If you're unfamiliar with them, they are covered in Chapter 4.) These are all variations on the same theme which, basically, mean that the value for money we get for our investments in human error improvement is limited by how well we *genuinely* understand why someone has done what they have done.

This understanding can *only* be achieved by talking to them in a way that makes them comfortable enough that they'll be honest with you. Again, I'll be coming back to the practicalities of this issue in the rest of the book.

So far, I've tried to make the case that an organisation needs its frontline managers proactively on site, looking for the inevitable safety and health issues that are always out there. However, whilst they are out on site looking for issues, it's also vital that they take the opportunity to effectively and proactively *lead* safety and health, and this chapter looks briefly at safety and health leadership.

HOW A GOOD SAFETY LEADER BEHAVES

Picture an office scene from the UK or US sitcom *The Office*. I'm not talking here about the lead character idiotic office manager, but instead the 'Gareth' character in the UK version – the slightly strange chap who's the closest thing on the show to a front-line supervisor. (If you haven't seen either version, he's a pompous, officious, deluded, self-important, gun-obsessed buffoon. And that's on a good day.) If you have ever watched the programme, you'll be well aware of the emotional response of the intelligent and sane 'nice one' who sits opposite and reports to him: incredulous and despairing at best, and utterly appalled at other times.

Can you imagine the reaction if this dubious 'Gareth' character was tasked with leading any sort of safety or health project or programme? Can I suggest that the likelihood of any sort of success would be zero, because the very *best* response he'd get from his colleagues would be total apathy? It's the real psychology behind this fictional example that is covered by the research I have based this book on.

It's often said that the difference between a leader and a manager is that leaders need followers, and that by definition, a good leader has *willing* followers. True, I'd argue, and very applicable to safety and health.

Leadership types: the Australian writer David Broadbent describes three types of leader, which frames this debate well, I think. He suggests some are 'firemen' (reactive), some are 'policemen' (compliance- and infraction-focused), and some are 'knights' (supervisors leading proactively from the front with passion, honour, and integrity.) This reactive/compliant/

proactive distinction mirrors perhaps the best model of culture: Parker and Hudson, as introduced previously.

The best-selling leadership writer Pat Lencioni says that the three essential virtues of leadership are humility, hard work, and emotional intelligence. (Note that humility is not being 'ever so 'umble', it's being ego-free.) Sam Walker's hugely readable book *Captain Class* (especially if you like sport), about the best sports teams and their leaders, makes the same points, but using the likes of Michael Jordan and Richie McCaw as examples. Sticking with the All-Black rugby team, James Kerr, in his book *Legacy*, covers very similar ground and reports that their one golden rule is 'no dick-heads', as they sour everything. (And we're back to *The Office*.)

In short, there is definitely broad agreement as to what good leadership and teamwork looks like! In behavioural terms, this includes:

- Leads by (good) example.
- Uses (sincere) praise as often as possible.
- Coaches (selling) when they can, rather than telling.
- Communicates clearly and impactfully.
- Actively involves the workforce in decision-making as much as possible, to empower them and to engender ownership.
- Sees what needs doing and has the drive to do it (person by person).

Perhaps the single most important element, however, is an objective understanding of human error, and an analytical and proactive approach to it. Chapter 4 addresses the mechanics of this directly, but please see the mainstream 'how to be excellent' books *Mindset* (Dweck), *Black Box Thinking* (Syed), *The Fearless Organisation* (Edmondson), and *The Culture Code* (Coyle). You win a prize if you can find anything in any of them that contradicts what Reason, Dekker, and others wrote decades ago, but it's great to see such growing consensus. (To be fair, Syed actually references Dekker).

In short, high levels of performance are generated in *any* aspect of work or enterprise led in this way. (The well-known analogy that explains why: pulling string is easy, but pushing it is next to impossible.) To link to an earlier chapter, it's largely through these behaviours that the workforce learn 'what we want, what we really want'. Apply them to productivity but not equally to safety and health, and you'll have a productive workforce rather than a safe and healthy one.

In the simplest terms, organisations with world class safety and health simply apply this approach to both productivity *and* safety and health.

LEADING BY EXAMPLE

Just one example of a leader not following the safety rules themselves gives a green light to anyone else not to follow them. It is an utter disaster for any safety and health culture. Managers who work really long hours and/or communicate top-down only set a clear example.

We'll talk about this in more detail later, in 'Setting the Tone'. For now, it's worth stating that (as discussed previously), ideally, there will be a minimum number of rules, and that these will be sensible, fair, and easy to follow. Why set yourself up to fail?

RECOGNITION, PRAISE, AND COACHING

Have you have ever watched the 'senior manager working undercover on the shop floor' programme *Undercover Boss*? They always end up saying, 'Ah, *now* I know what I need to do', don't they? I once made a point of counting how many of the bosses claimed to have learnt a huge amount. It was all of them, of course, and it illustrates the point that we best learn about the ins and outs of a job from talking to the person who actually *does* the job.

This may seem so self-evidently obvious that it doesn't need saying. However, it begs the question: why has nearly every workforce I've ever talked to said, 'Management don't talk to us enough'? (I joke at 'lead metric' conferences that the very best one of them all is to sit near workers and count how many times they say 'I could have bloody told them'.)

This 'learning' element is a key theme of the book (see the next chapter). However, the main point I'd like to make here is that, although all the 'undercover boss' employees smiled widely when told they were getting a pay rise, a good 50 per cent actually welled up in gratitude when told how great they were, and how pleased the boss was to have someone so special work for them. This is because genuine recognition reaches us more deeply than reward. It taps into something more primeval and powerful than money.

Thinking Fast and Slow : here, I will offer a brief review of the only psychology book to win a Nobel prize. Daniel Kahneman's aforementioned book covers how we have a logical front brain and the *millions*-of-years-old back brain. We're prone to assuming that the 'recently'-developed 'thinking' bit dominates, but actually, the neural pathways back to front are much stronger than front to back. What this means is that what should be fact-based decision-making is often instinctive, decision-based fact selection (or even creation). More positively, we can work with this when we seek to reach hearts as well as minds.

Another good example of this would be the Ryder Cup golf match between Europe and the USA. Technically it's an exhibition match, but in September 2012, I watched an American golfer who had calmly won *11 million dollars* just the week before the event look close to a heart attack on the final day of the team event, playing for no money at all. If you read one of the best-ever golf books *A Good Walk Spoiled*, which starts with a Ryder Cup story, you'll know that it's because he almost certainly *was* close to a heart attack. Some things are far more important than money, and letting the 'tribe' down is one of them.

We'll return to address the practical aspects of this theme in Section Two.

WORKFORCE INVOLVEMENT (AND OBJECTIVE ANALYSIS)

It's said that 'a person most owns what they helped create' because of investment of time and effort. Another saying that resonates with me suggests,

> *I'll only impose my idea on you if it's four times better than yours, as you'll work three times harder on your own idea than you will on mine.*

As mentioned previously, the old saying is that pushing string is impossible, but pulling it is easy. Well, this is true unless it's frozen (with fear perhaps?), in which case we can push it where we want it to go – but then can't do much with it when we get there. It's a good analogy, and we really do need to proactively work with these truths of personality and people and not fight against them.

But perhaps the most vital element of workforce involvement is that they simply know the day-to-day realities far better than we ever will. It is 'their job' to know, of course. The key element of any good learning process is, as mentioned previously, tapping into the knowledge behind the comment we so often hear mumbled in a canteen: 'I could have told them that years ago, if they'd only bothered to ask'. Reflecting this eternal truth objective analysis is covered in great detail in Section Two of this book.

In short, once you've analysed what's wrong with your systems or understood exactly why the workforce aren't behaving as you'd like, it really helps if the solutions come from the workforce themselves.

THE *OUTPUT* OF TRANSFORMATIONAL LEADERSHIP

It's worth listing the consequences of treating people in a 'transformational' way, as it illustrates clearly how the *general* culture benefits and why we should take the trouble to do it.

In the United States they talk about 'discretionary behaviour', and it's stated that without it, an organisation simply *cannot* develop a strong culture, as they will never get beyond 'compliant'. (In Chapter One, we discussed the limitations of compliance.) In the UK, we might refer to these as behaviours as 'above-the-line behaviour' or 'organisational citizenship behaviours', but regardless of the collective name we give them, we are talking about behaviours such as:

- Volunteering to be part of a project or process team or to be a safety rep.
- Volunteering to be a mental health first aider.
- Noticing a change in behaviour in a colleague and asking them if they're OK.
- Undertaking non-mandatory safety training or attending non-mandatory meetings.
- Paying any sort of genuine attention or contributing to a discussion during *mandatory* training or meetings.
- Saying something to a colleague who has put themselves at risk.
- Making an effort to model safe behaviours and practices in front of new starts.
- Taking the time to show new starts the ropes.
- Stopping to clear a housekeeping issue.
- Stopping to call a 'time out' because you're not comfortable with a safety issue.
- Reporting a near miss.
- Responding honestly to questions during an incident investigation.

And so on.

'OK, fewer of our best staff are leaving. A reduction in absenteeism and presenteeism. More creativity, discretionary effort, productivity, and a better reputation . . . granted . . . but apart from that . . .'

As we've already stressed several times, few organisations that have all the systems, training, and procedures in place to have acquired compliance certificates on their reception walls are anywhere near as *genuinely compliant* on a daily basis as they'd like to be, so to deliberately blur the edges between compliance

Figure 2.1 What has this wellbeing ever done for us?

and 'discretionary behaviour', we could describe discretionary behaviour as: complying with a safety requirement when not supervised or when working alone.

Because, as we said at the start, often what should be compliance is actually discretionary – especially if it's late or you're working from a van a long way from base.

Regardless of blurred edges, I hope that you'd agree the list in the previous section is simply the basic behaviours we'd all like to see our workforce undertaking. It's certainly what we want when we get inspirational speakers in or launch a 'hearts and minds' initiative.

THREE FINAL CONCEPTS: NUDGES, GUERRILLA WARFARE, AND THE 'MINDFUL' SAFETY CULTURE

This short section attempts to summarise some of the most leading-edge thinking that sets the context for this entire book:

- The vital *symbolic* importance of key behaviours and events.
- The importance of always being mindful that safety and health is an ongoing 'guerrilla war'.
- The 'mindful' culture.

TOILET BOWLS IN AMSTERDAM: 'NUDGE' THEORY AND HOW QUICKLY WE CAN COMMUNICATE WHAT WE REALLY WANT (FOR GOOD OR BAD!)

If you've already heard of nudge theory, you'll know that the most famous example is the well-placed painted ceramic fly on the Amsterdam toilet bowl (Figure 2.2) that most of us men can't help but aim at. This apparently reduces splashing by a full 50 per cent, with associated savings in cleaning costs and the environmental impact of cleaning chemicals. (Seriously, imagine trying to match that improvement with a new rule, training, or supervision!) A seldom-mentioned but, I think, utterly vital element of the Amsterdam case study is that the person who came up with the idea is the person who cleaned the toilets!

Figure 2.2 The fly in the urinal
Source: © Ruslan Kudrin/Dreamstime.com

'Nudge' theory is a hugely influential concept at the moment, with the UK government and the UK Health & Safety Laboratory have a team dedicated to its application. Examples include empty police vans parked near potential trouble spots, tax forms asking, 'Are you sure you haven't forgotten anything?' (it's far harder to lie directly than to pretend to forget), and motorway signs saying, 'Don't litter – other people don't', which is a nudge with reference to social norms.

Of course, the concept of 'nudging' isn't new. If you've ever used paint to mark a floor or a wall to make clear where something goes (or doesn't go), you've arguably used the nudge concept. Though I may be in danger of trampling over academic definitions, in essence I think of it as *any* small and/or simple thing that can have a big influence on people's behaviour.

As previously discussed, the word 'but' in the middle of a sentence is a good example. Have you ever been told 'you're a really nice person and I really like you, but . . .' and had that sentence end well?! This is because we always put the important part of the message after the 'but'. We all know very well that when we have a sentence start well, but then contain a 'but', there's a problem coming. However, it doesn't need to be something we're aware of, as it can influence us at a subconscious level. (The subconscious 'back brain' gets it clearly.) If told, 'This job needs doing safely *but* by Friday', both parties may be unaware of how the real message was communicated – but communicated it is, as you'll almost certainly get the job by Friday as safely as is viable.

Three famous mainstream examples of small things having a big impact:

UK magician Derren Brown has a trick where he leaves a full wallet in the middle of a busy pavement, but inside a red painted circle – then saunters back to pick it up untouched an hour later, as people will not reach across the red line.

In the UK in September 2012, a senior government politician had an argument with a policeman, during which he allegedly called the policeman a 'pleb' (it's not a swear word, but is a highly derogatory UK term for a person perceived to be of lower social class). Just one word, but it generated a huge amount of negative feeling and reaction. His entire political party dropped several points in the opinion polls, and his political career seemed over. 'Always choose your words carefully' remains sage advice, as the bosses of the Tokyo Olympics and KPMG found out in early 2021. That said, in contrast, Donald Trump has recently shown that you can say whatever you want, any way you want, and still have 74 million people vote for you. Freud himself would struggle with this one.

Related is the concept of the 'critical incident' which tells us that *little* things can mean, and teach us, a *lot*. These aren't necessarily 'nudges' as defined by the textbooks, but I'd like to include them, as the important point is that they may not look important at a glance but their impact is big.

In short, a politician simply couldn't have blurted out the word 'pleb' without holding an underlying sense of social superiority. In fact, that it popped out *under stress* makes it even more damning.

The jeweller Gerald Ratner saw his company's share value drop to £0.02, and was sacked by his own board, after describing his own jewellery as 'crap'. His customers already knew this, of course, but this indignity nudged huge numbers of them over a line that made buying anything else from him totally unpalatable. (Incidentally, I shared a conference stage with him once – he was extremely funny about the events that he brought on himself, rolling out lines like, 'So we ended up owing the banks a total of *one billion pounds* . . . (pause) . . . which *back in those days*, of course, was *a lot* of money!')

CRITICAL INCIDENTS, NUDGES, AND SAFETY AND HEALTH

Managers who fail to follow their own safety rules throw a big negative nudge, as it's often said that the worst level you set as a leader is the highest level you can expect from your reports. Other examples might include starting a meeting by saying 'elf and safety first, of course', clearly meaning it is to be got out of the way before the important issues can be addressed.

More positively, many years ago, Shell and others stopped asking the question, 'Why did you choose to shut down?' and started to ask instead, 'Why did you think it safe to start back up?' You'll note that the technical information in the reports will be the same: 'This happened and we thought this was the cause, so we thought . . .' but the shadow it throws is entirely different. The first is taken to mean, 'You'd better have a good reason for that, because it's career defining if it isn't one that I like'.

Another classic and oft-repeated experiment shows that if a person observes a prosocial act (like helping an elderly person across the road), they are significantly more likely to undertake that act the next time they have the chance. Importantly, they are highly unlikely to be conscious of the reason for their behaviour, and we've already talked about peer influence and how behaviour breeds behaviour – positively as well as negatively.

This book is, I hope, full of references to 'nudges' – small things which make a big difference. In short, if the commitment to excellence isn't there, then the workforce will know. If it is, we should actively find ways of proactively communicating that to the workforce.

A good quality 'walk and talk' is the perfect vehicle to nudge colleagues in the right direction. A manager who asks a supervisor, 'So all production issues are under control. That's great, but how are *you*?' once a week is considerably more likely to have a supervisor who asks their workforce the same question.

SAFETY IS NOT AN ACADEMIC EXERCISE, IT'S A 'GUERRILLA WAR'

Reason's famous Swiss cheese model (Figure 2.3) shows that the more weaknesses there are in an organisation – from strategy management decisions, through supervision and process safety through to individual actions – the more likely the holes in the slices of Swiss cheese are to line up, and an accident to occur.

This model shows that *with the benefit of hindsight*, all accidents could have been prevented, and it has directly influenced the various 'target zero' campaigns. The model is not without criticism, being linear as it is, but it is hugely influential, and I've seen it used in many fields including addiction treatment.

I once gave a talk to a shipbuilder about the Swiss cheese model and, after thinking about its strategic implications for a while, they approached me and commented, 'We discussed this over coffee, and all agree we should never have agreed to build this ship this way'.

Similarly, Reason's 'knot in the rubber band' model illustrates why the target zero campaigns can prove so controversial. (I wish I had a pound for every heated debate about whether target zero is best seen as a *concept*.)

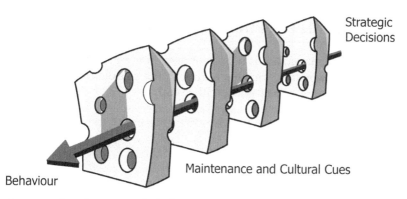

Strategic Decisions

Maintenance and Cultural Cues

Behaviour

Successive layers of defences, barriers, and safeguards

Figure 2.3 The Swiss cheese model

Source: Adapted from James Reason, 2008

Before we explore that, we need to quickly consider the role of hindsight.

The hindsight model (see Figure 2.4) illustrates that with hindsight, the negative outcome that we are investigating looks inevitable as A follows B follows C. However, if we put ourselves in the shoes of the individuals concerned, we'll often see that, *at the time,* several other outcomes looked (and indeed *were*) equally likely. Only *after* the event does the sequence seem inevitable.

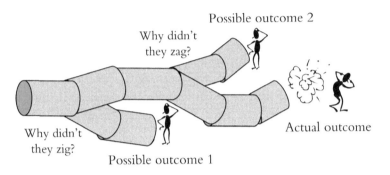

Figure 2.4 Hindsight model

Source: © Sidney Dekker, 2006

THE 'KNOT IN THE RUBBER BAND' MODEL

Risk management is not about designing out all risk, it's about proportionality. Imagine a knot in the middle of a large rope and a tug-of-war team on either end.

Photo 2.1 Knot in the rubber band

When the left-hand side is winning, the company is very safe; when the right-hand side is winning, then the company is running too much risk. When the knot is in the middle, then there is a genuine balance of safety and productivity. (This, of course, a version of the famous 'balanced scorecard' concept.)

Reason says that it's easy in theory, but once we start work in the modern world, then all sorts of pressures will automatically try and pull the rope away from balance – such as changes in material prices, contractors who don't perform as they promised they would, and unexpected delays. (Five years ago, who saw Brexit, Trump, and a global pandemic coming?). But it doesn't have to be an infamous 'black swan' that causes problems; a few white swans swimming in harmony will do just fine! (The concept of a 'black swan' is being used more and more in articles and the media to describe where something unlikely but devastating actually happens. BP's Deepwater Horizon and the Japanese tsunami are famous examples. It is used to encourage in-depth 'what if?' worst-case scenario thinking.)

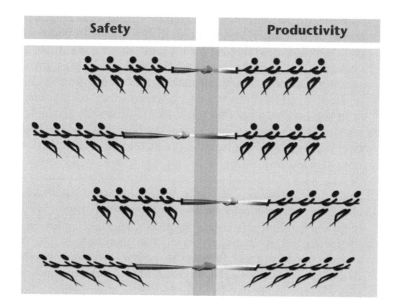

Figure 2.5 The knot in the rubber band

Source: Adapted from Reason, 2008

The key is to not ever become overstretched so that the knot moves from a position of genuine balance and the company becomes vulnerable. When vulnerable, an incident is more likely, of course, and investigators will take a dim view if investigations show that the organisation had overstretched and was indeed 'an accident waiting to happen'.

THESE MODELS: HUMAN NATURE AND MENTAL HEALTH

At conferences I like to get audience members to jump on stage and take the rope, tug-of-war style (initially this was to 'add energy and to make the learning point memorable' – see Photo 2.1). I noticed, however, that they always wanted to actually *have* a tug of war, with many starting this spontaneously. I thought I could work with this, and learnt to set it up with North v South 'teams', or US v UK or UK v Europe, etc, so that 'nearly always' became always!

Not only do the teams always 'go for it' enthusiastically, but the audience will always encourage 'their team' with cheers and shouts. Before anyone gets hurt, I jump in, grab the rope, and point out that 'if you want people to do unsafe things, then all you need to do is ask them nicely', and that the individuals on stage were the keen ones who were fastest to volunteer to jump up and help me out. (So 'bosses – just sack all the keen ones!'). The analogy is that it's not the person in the rope exercise that causes all the trouble, it's the person in charge of the rope exercise.

The implications for mental health are obvious. We all know about the importance of balance and resilience, but achieving them on a daily basis is less easy. As a species, we are easily distracted, and really like to get stuck in and crack on. We can't entirely design out risk, because as a species, we don't just have risk tolerance, we have risk appetite. Many of the people our C suites least want to lose have the biggest such appetites. I think an adaptation of Reason's most famous model shows exactly where 'good work' fits into the individual resilience piece.

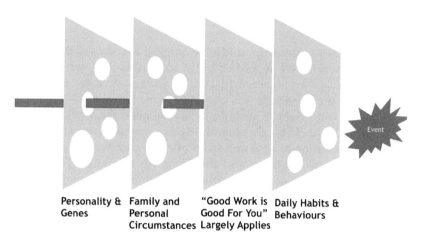

Personality & Genes
Family and Personal Circumstances
"Good Work is Good For You" Largely Applies
Daily Habits & Behaviours

Figure 2.6 Reason's Swiss cheese model adapted

Source: Anker & Marsh

Figure 2.6 shows an adaptation of Reason's Swiss cheese model that reflects the fact that 'good work is good for you'. As organisations, we can't control what happens when our employees go home (though we can send them home in a good mood, hoping for virtuous, not vicious, circles!) but we do have control of their working environment. Some careers are associated with depression and suicidal behaviour, but there are several examples where problems occur mostly once they have *left*. Soldiers and cricketers are two. Professional cricketers spend huge amounts of time essentially just bantering with their peers. They banter even during a match, if they're not batting or standing together in the slips and, of course, when waiting for it to stop raining. When they retire, they really miss this camaraderie. Similarly, despite the hardships and risks soldiers tend to struggle when they are ex-soldiers.

Two statements I consider unarguable: good work is good for you, and can save your life. Good leaders are nearly always key to good work.

PRACTICAL APPLICATION

To return to my shipbuilding example, we can say that in an ideal world, we wouldn't build ships this way, but it is, of course, *not* an ideal world. A more pragmatic view would be to say that *somebody* was bound to agree to build the ship this way, so it might as well be us, as we need the work. Consequently, pockets of vulnerability are *inevitably* going to pop up from time to time and from place to place even if, overall, the culture is strong and the planning thorough. The trick, then, is to be geared to spot these emerging vulnerabilities quickly and respond promptly. This is entirely analogous to the key principles of UK HSG 48, which covers human error and says:

- Design the job so that error is unlikely.
- Make sure you have mechanisms in place to spot it when it (inevitably) happens.
- Make sure you can respond quickly.

(This also illustrated by the basic tug-of-war exercise above). Following on from this, Reason suggests safety is best thought of as an on-going *guerrilla war*. Like any such war, you can't win it in the long run, but you can delay defeat almost inevitably. To do this, you'll need keen intelligence and data, and to use whatever resources you have at your disposal cleverly.

Some managers I've spoken to report that although they buy into the *concept* of target zero, the *reality* can seem daunting – even de-motivating. If you have 20,000 workers worldwide, then the first lost-time injury is likely to arrive early in the new year, no matter how excellent your safety standards. What's vital is that you don't become despondent and fatalistic about this reality, and the rubber band model seems to be one that managers find best expresses their experience of the ongoing dynamic.

This book is, of course, intended as a pocket guide on 'how to fight an effective guerrilla safety and health war' – starting with the realisation that the principles of HSG 48 apply to organisational and individual resilience.

SUMMARY OF KEY POINTS

This section has made the case that day-to-day behaviour is vital, whether it is directly determining the risk levels or helping set the tone and therefore helping trigger others' risky, or safe, behaviour. It stresses that there is always bad news to be found, and that the best companies proactively seek these weaknesses out rather than wait for the weaknesses to find them. This is equally true of mental health and wellbeing as it is of safety.

SUGGESTED ISSUES TO DISCUSS

I know that some readers will look at the reference section and order books so that they can read up on some theories outlined above. Others, on the other hand, will be very keen to move onto something more practical. With the latter particularly in mind, I'd like to end this first half of the book with a suggested list of questions and/or issues that any manager can consider at any time. I'm hoping these will also work as a review of points raised.

I'll absolutely *guarantee* one thing, however. Even if you're working in an organisation with a proactive focus and a genuinely strong safety culture, you won't like *all* the answers!

Ask yourself:

- Do people know who is responsible for each element of the safety and health process or do 'two people think they are, so no one actually is'?
- Are toolbox talks and weekly briefs clear, user-friendly, and with understanding confirmed (not just knocked off with a 'sign here' – it's your signature I need and I'm not too bothered if you don't even speak the language in question)?
- Do risk assessments involve genuine reflection and objective thought? Or are they more 'photocopy, sign, file'?
- Is it easy to communicate concerns upwards, or does the organisational structure make this difficult, if not totally impossible? For example, what do people do if they need to go *through* the person they're concerned about, especially if

this is an interpersonal issue? (And they know for a fact their boss is *not* going to see this as a learning opportunity!)

- Are the people responsible for writing systems and procedures empowered to ensure they are actually followed?
- Do the people who write the systems and procedures actively consult the end users as a systematic part of the design process?
- Do 'good news audits' produce an automatic sceptical response, as lots of infamous incidents were preceded by a string of positive audits – for example, Piper Alpha? (It's worth remembering the Andrew Hopkins quote, 'A string of continuous good news? That's not realistic and *really* should set alarm bells ringing!')
- Do we proactively look at the trends in the reporting system? Are there divisions, shifts, or other demographics that hardly ever report? If so, this probably isn't good news – dig into it and find out what the blockages are and why.
- Conversely, has someone raised a safety or wellbeing issue that was basically ignored? (This is a characteristic of nearly all major incidents.)
- Consider how senior management respond to *bad* news. A response as simple as simply *looking* inconvenienced is problematic. (I once asked an MD at a board meeting if he ever responded negatively to a safety issue being raised, and he was adamant, 'Never!' I asked, 'Not even with the eyes?', and the whole room burst into laughter, as he was notorious for this. Luckily, he wasn't a defensive man – he laughed at himself, and we were off.)
- Follow an incident that is mentioned in conversation through the reporting system. How far did it get? What was learned? What was the done with this learning? Even the best companies with highly expensive tracking systems will find that the answers to these questions are concerning.
- When looking at the analysis that flows from incidents, imagine you have a big red 'why?' stamp. Do any points noted beg asking this question? If so, the investigation probably hasn't gone deep enough and you're targeting a symptom, not a root cause. (NB: someone being signed off with 'stress' is an incident.)
  - Consider where the *number* of 'walk and talks' is monitored but not the *quality*. Where this is the case, you'll often

find that, in order to meet targets, a flurry of poor-quality ones are undertaken at the end of the month.

- Ask if there has been any cost-cutting recently – or perhaps a 'renegotiated' contract. If so, was it risk assessed really thoroughly for the 'law of unintended consequences', or were assumptions made that all will be well? With that law in mind, it's always worth checking who is being rewarded for what. Some examples:

  o Procurement are rewarded for cutting costs, but no one checks if any false economies result as a consequence (e.g., cheaper PPE that no one actually wears because it's uncomfortable or isn't fit for purpose; cheap components that fail and leak; manpower cuts that mean there is genuinely not enough time to thoroughly think, plan and check).

  o Bonuses that focus attention on only one aspect of excellence. (An example of this may be found at Texas City, where the findings of the wide-ranging Baker report into the explosion at the BP plant in 2005 could be summarised as, 'They put so much effort into making sure no one tripped over, then used these figures as *proof* of excellent safety standards – even in the face of maintenance cuts that led to the place blowing up'.)

  o Look at the way contractors are remunerated and selected – because as you well know, the term 'a whole can of worms' was probably coined with subcontractors in mind. The old saying 'you can have it cheap, quick, or good quality – please pick any two of the three' summarises the issue perfectly.

And last but certainly not least:

  o Use metrics that look at the human factor. Use cultural measurement tools. Ask, what are fatigue levels like? How engaged and empowered are the workforce? (Some basic suggested items are suggested later in the book.)

CONCLUSION

The list above is not exhaustive, of course, but it should give anyone plenty to be mindful about! You can see that its primary aim is to imbue a sceptical, proactive, and thoughtful mindset that is far in advance of a manager who's merely been trained in the legislation of compliance. It's the mindset of a streetwise guerrilla fighter, if you like Reason's analogy.

Some training may well be required so that your frontline supervisors understand the *why* behind the mindset, as well as the *what*. However, with Scott Geller's memorable training v education example in mind, we still need a mechanism to genuinely embed this mindset. (Geller stresses that good *training* is much more in-depth and hands-on than basic education. To illustrate the point, he asks how we'd feel if our teenage children came home from school announcing that, next week, they will be doing sex education – but, over their shoulder as they leave the room, they add that once that education bit is done, they'll be moving on to some *training* . . .)

Aristotle observed that humour is merely common sense speeded up. We laugh because instantly, we know exactly what Geller means here. The question for the reader is, how often have you seen a session that really should have been a *training* session for a limited number of workers, that was instead a short briefing session for many more?

So, ideally, introduced with some suitable *training*, we need to roll out a robust, user-friendly, and simple 'walk and talk' approach that is based on objective analysis, open and honest communication, and which allows the whole workforce a regular opportunity to contribute to the safety and health culture. Section Two outlines a simple five-step model that aims to achieve this.

Section two

Safety & health contacts

The dedicated safety and health contact involves (up to) five simple but distinct phases. To be more specific, it needs an appropriate *combination* of the following five phases:

1 Introduce yourself, break the ice, and set the tone.
2 Analysis.
3 Coaching.
4 Eliciting a promise (if required).
5 Closing out.

One of the aims of this book is to provide the reader with some tools to help them decide what 'appropriate' means in any individual situation.

'WALK AND TALK' OVERVIEW (BEHAVIOURAL SAFETY EXCELLENCE, INSPIRATIONAL SPEAKERS, AND THE 'WALK AND TALK')

This book steals liberally from proven behavioural safety methodologies, as we know from hard-won experience what effective and ineffective methodologies look like! This applies perhaps most obviously to the second step of a 'walk and talk' – *analysis*.

I'm arguing that a really good 'walk and talk' process is, even in isolation, an excellent behavioural safety process, and is equally an excellent wellbeing process. I'll try to expand and illustrate.

We've found that an excellent way of objectively understanding the issue at hand is through limited time duration *project* teams who are trained in behavioural analysis techniques and who are allowed to choose issues they want to address. Any 'high-impact, low-cost' solutions they come back with should be implemented as soon as possible, and as much mileage as possible made of them in in-house magazines and other internal communication channels.

These project teams can address anything and everything (see Lean, Scrum, and Six Sigma methodologies, etc). They can certainly address the key themes of mental health and wellbeing (fatigue, engagement, systemic psycho-social stressors, and the like).

In addition, with behavioural safety, some form of *ongoing* peer-to-peer observation process might be also adopted to target and track the changes the analysis process generates. If an ongoing observation process is used, then the behavioural measurement from this might be used to provide data for feedback charts. This is what is often referred to as 'full' behavioural safety. It has its roots in the quality work of WE Deming, and has much in common with Six Sigma methodologies. To give you a flavour of what I mean, imagine the following workforce-run canteen meeting with a health and safety theme:

> *As you know, the volunteer committee decided to look at PPE initially, and the collated score from the unannounced measures we've been taking over the last month is 66%, as can be seen on the big colourful chart on the wall here. Now, in the first week, people hurriedly put their PPE on as we approached, but once you all realised scores were just an anonymous tick in the box, you all settled down. We've discounted that first week, and feel these scores are accurate – based on a suitably sized and randomised sample as they are. We'll update that chart on a weekly basis. Now, the question is what can we realistically get up to by the end of next month, and most importantly, what are the obstacles to getting there?*

And suggestions about remote dispensers and better quality PPE that doesn't mist up will fly in, but the key element of any enhancement approach reflects the basic premise of the Safety Differently approach: namely, "I want you to be safe and healthy as well as productive – and you want to be safe, healthy and productive. What do you need?"

Two expressions that contain great truth: One, if we can measure it, we can manage it; and two, what gets measured gets done. That said, I'd argue that the main use of measurement in great 'behavioural safety' is to help identify what needs targeting with analysis, and to then track the quality of that analysis.

In short, a systemic 'walk and talk' process based on analysis and coaching will be 100 times as effective in reducing unsafe behaviour in the medium-to-long term as an 'if you can walk on hot coals you can do anything, so go back to the shop floor and be safe' inspirational initiative. (I can say this – my business partner is Jason Anker, MBE, who many would consider Europe's premier inspirational speaker.) We both argue that good human error reduction is something that improves that behaviour in a *sustainable* manner. An inspirational speaker or emotional DVD is an excellent way to raise awareness and motivation, but neither is sustainable. Use them to raise volunteers who can contribute to something analysis based!

Similarly, the essence of a good wellbeing approach in the medium-to-long term is objectively understanding what can be done to encourage and facilitate. A 'walk and talk' is central to that.

SUGGESTED FREQUENCY OF SAFETY CONTACTS

Aubrey Daniels, in *Safe by Accident?*, stresses that there are three levels of learning: there's basic learning, then mastery of the basics, and then, finally, *fluency*. Basic learning involves someone knowing how to do a task, and being able to do it without fault with a lot of concentration. 'Mastery' can be described as, 'I can now do it with a degree of confidence', and tends to be achieved after 30 or so practices. For example, imagine learning to play golf or work as a volunteer on the Samaritans' helpline – or any other skill. At what stage would you stop saying 'I'm learning to' and start saying 'I am a . . .'? For example, on a helpline, if you volunteer twice a week, you'll probably think yourself broadly competent and experienced after a few months or so.

Fluency, however, describes the stage when these skills are embedded to a similar extent to your driving skills – when you've been driving for years. I like to think I'm a reasonably fluent speaker at conferences these days, but it took a few years, and I'm certainly better now than I was once I'd done my first 30 and had become broadly competent.

This notion of *fluency* is addressed by another US safety writer, Scott Geller, who says that safety must be something truly embedded as part of the very DNA of a company. (As in, 'Our culture is what we do around here, *automatically*'.) It needs to be embedded as a core *value* – because if there *is* a number one **priority**, it's making enough profit or generating enough turnover to stay in business (or, if it's an animal charity, it's raising funds and rescuing animals, etc).

Many battle-proven quotes like those just mentioned reference safety directly, but just substitute in the word 'care', and they apply to wellbeing too. For example, a genuinely embedded core value of care was well illustrated by the 'around the world' sailor Pete Goss when he turned back to rescue a fellow competitor in the Arctic. His inspirational talk builds to a simple question from the audience, which is, 'How long did it take you to abandon the month-long race and turn back when you realised it had to be you?' His answer: 'Oh, four or five seconds; it's the values of the sea. I didn't even need to think about it'. (His challenge is, 'Can you match that with your own statements at work?', and from the uneasy shuffling in the audience, it was clear not many felt they could.)

Another good example of embedded behaviour might be the yard manager of a mine who reminded me to reverse park one day. He did it in a naturally comfortable and friendly way that told me he'd done it many times before. As I looked around, I was very embarrassed to note that I was the only person out of around 200 not to have reverse parked! They'd already embedded that behaviour as a company – and I didn't make that mistake again!

Which all leads up to me returning to a point made previously: what do you imagine we think when companies tell us they have management's commitment to undertake at least one or two safety and health contacts a year!? Even doing one a month means it will take you around three years to reach basic mastery. So, I'd like to suggest that doing one formally once a month is an absolute *minimum* – not one that'll at all impress Peter McKie, the consultant from the previous section! Better still, of course, simply make 'what do you need to be safe and healthy?' and 'how *are* you?' questions a *daily* habit, part of any conversation. It'll transform the culture, and you'll all be broadly competent within a month or two. (Again: mental health first aiders are great, but, I'd argue, largely unnecessary if *everyone* has had some training and is looking out for each other.)

This is important for another reason as well. If our trainee supervisors and managers do not go out and use the techniques we've requested and trained them in, how can we give them feedback and embed the behaviours?

EMBEDDING TRAINING: WHO AND WHAT

A basic motivation theory developed by Victor Vroom explains why so many training courses are a waste of money (Figure S2.1). To be effective, training first needs to explain *what* we want people to do, and be clear *who* needs to do it (so that the expression 'If two people think they're responsible then no one is' doesn't apply).

WHY

However, we also need to take the trouble to explain *why*, or the average worker might well be bemused, and may well feel patronised and hence apt to drag their heels. No one likes to be told 'because I say so', even when they are only ten years old. More than this, without an appreciation of the reasoning behind a requested behaviour or action, we aren't well placed to adjust when something unexpected happens (to refer back to the concept of operational dexterity).

61

HOW

We then need to address 'how' to do what we want them to do, because if an employee is worried that they can't do something competently, then given any leeway at all, they'll be apt to find any excuse not to do it at all, in case they make a fool of themselves.

This is especially so in the area of mental health, where people are reluctant to engage others in case they 'get it wrong' and 'make matters worse'. Having a professional explain that actually, you *can't* get it wrong is very reassuring. 'Asking someone if they are thinking of hurting themselves won't prompt them into doing, so though may get you an indignant "no! of course not!" But if they *are*, then you might just save their life'. (In the next section, we introduce the technique of asking more simply 'how are you?' twice. First rhetorically, and the second time with meaning, once some rapport is established.)

VALUED OUTCOME – WHAT'S IN IT FOR ME?

Finally, we need to consider whether the individual sees any *value* in the outcome we seek –whether that's analysis, praising, coaching, or challenging. Importantly, we need to think of this combination of *'what and why'*, *'how'*, and *'perceived as valued'* as not something we stack on top of each other, but rather as something we *multiply* – so a low score *anywhere* means a low score overall, and motivation will be poor.

It's vital that the typical front-line supervisor be taught to value the outcome of these behaviours by the organisation. A hugely experienced S&H professional of my acquaintance summarises it thus:

> *If the behaviours requested are not considered career enhancing in the smoke shack and canteen six months after the training course, then they won't be happening, and you'll have wasted your bloody time and money.*
>
> (Well put, Ken F!)

Vroom

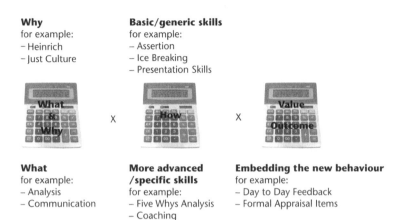

Why	**Basic/generic skills**	
for example:	for example:	
– Heinrich	– Assertion	
– Just Culture	– Ice Breaking	
	– Presentation Skills	

What   **More advanced**   **Embedding the new behaviour**

What	**More advanced**	**Embedding the new behaviour**
for example:	**/specific skills**	for example:
– Analysis	for example:	– Day to Day Feedback
– Communication	– Five Whys Analysis	– Formal Appraisal Items
	– Coaching	

Figure S2.1 Vroom/Marsh model

We achieve this through *formal* and *informal* feedback. Formal feedback involves giving safety and health items prominence in the appraisal – some companies don't include these in the formal appraisal at all, or give them only perfunctory coverage on the day (by which I mean both the appraiser and the person being appraised clearly relax a little through these items whilst collecting their thoughts, before getting back to the important stuff! As an experiment, try videoing a session and playing it back with the sound off, rating the participants' animation!)

Informal feedback can be summarised with our adaptation of Aubrey Daniels' 'tick' rating. He suggests when we see a worker doing something right, we make a tick. However, should we see a supervisor praising a worker for doing something right (as requested on a recent leadership course perhaps), it's worth two ticks. A manager taking the time to praise a supervisor he's seen praising a worker doing something right gets three ticks! I'm sure you get the idea. It's in *this* way the top-down commitment is reinforced, and the behaviours we want more of are *embedded* as 'the way we do things around here' – it's not from neatly filing away the training course appraisal scores, no matter how good they are.

The reverse would be a manager seeing a supervisor fail to challenge an unwanted act, or praise a novel positive one (as requested on a recent course), and saying nothing. No ticks for anyone, and no embedded behaviour change will be at all likely, either.

FOLLOW UP

A useful technique is to produce a simple set of scales addressing the key behaviours requested during a training course, then ask some of the workers to rate them. For example:

How do you rate your supervisor's 'care' for your welfare?

5 Often asks after my wellbeing, and certainly would if I looked quiet or a bit frazzled and manic.

4

3 Would ask if I was unusually quiet or manic.

2

1 Would never ask, no matter what!

(A suggested basic seven-item checklist is included in Appendix 2.)

These scores can be collated with the scores of other items addressing such issues as challenging, coaching, leading by example, involving the workforce, and analysis. This makes for a much better training efficacy metric than simple 'happy-sheets'.

Done thoroughly, an organisation will too often find itself pondering an extremely disappointing overall score. In addition, it will be highly likely that safety climate and culture surveys will be showing little improvement, anecdotal evidence will be suggesting 'things don't feel all that different', and accident rates and other KPIs (turnover, absenteeism) will be inching rather than leaping forward, if at all, and broadly demonstrating the infamous 'plateaued wave' – sometimes slightly above, and sometimes slightly below, a straight line.

I would like to make the assertion that, in my experience, in the medium-to-long term, *at least 80 per cent* of the efficacy of a training course is in the follow up and embedding (any hard research data is very much welcome. Any interested students, please do get in touch).

In short, we need to:

- Train our managers and supervisors in *what* to do and who's to do it.
- Explain *why* they need to do it.
- Give them the *skills* and tools to ensure they can do them *well*.
- Ensure they do them *often* enough to master the basics.

And:

- Give them systemic feedback to ensure they refine and *embed* these behaviours, and become skilled and fluent in them.

BEFORE HIS INTERPERSONAL SKILLS TRAINING, PAUL'S ATTEMPTS AT CHALLENGING UNSAFE BEHAVIOUR DIDN'T ALWAYS WORK OUT

CHAPTER 3

Introduce yourself and set the tone

In this section I will discuss:

- Ice-breaking.
- Setting the tone.
- Building trust.
- Leading by example.

Though it's alluded to frequently, this isn't a book that directly talks about 'emotional intelligence', or the vital importance of soft skills and transformational leadership in setting the tone of a caring and empowering culture generally. There are lots of techniques of vital importance (listening, feedback) that are only touched on briefly. That's merely to try and keep the book concise, and you can feel safe in the knowledge that there are lots of other books that cover this material really well. It's also highly likely that your HR or training department have excellent courses that would dovetail perfectly with 'walk and talk' training.

FIRST, SOMETHING HUGELY IMPORTANT – MODELLING (OR 'DON'T BE THE T*T WITH THE TOUPEE')

A golden rule of leadership is that we are all leading by example at all times, whether we intend to be or not – so it's worth doing it well. A hugely welcome and positive change in recent times has been for leaders to talk about mental health issues. There's an ever-growing appreciation of the fact that keeping quiet whilst promoting campaigns that stress 'it's good to talk' and 'it's OK to not be OK' is an opportunity lost, and an initiative undermined.

So, a key thing you *must always do* yourself is to model safety and health at all times – not just when talking about the subject. It's

DOI: 10.4324/9781003177784-6

often said that the highest standard you can expect from those that work for you is the lowest standard you set yourself. All managers and supervisors are role models, whether they like it or not (as are safety representatives, experienced workers, and the charismatic individuals who are admired in the canteen).

One of our clients had the former UK Prime Minister Gordon Brown visit a site (Figure 3.1) and decline to wear eye protection during a site visit. Management let him get away with it because of the inconvenience of refusing to walk him about, but they wished they hadn't. The CEO still says, 'I've paid for that decision every day since. The lads didn't say, as we hoped, "I'd have done the same if I'd been in Vick's shoes" . . . they leapt on it with glee, and every toolbox talk and briefing, and *especially* at any disciplinary hearing, we get "what about Gordon Brown!". If I could turn the clock back, I would!'

Figure 3.1 Gordon Brown visits Govan

Source: © Getty Images

The following is a personal experience that you might find amusing.

One of our clients had a visit from a senior chap from HQ, who flatly refused to don his hard hat during a site visit. The local admin team quickly spoke to their contacts at HQ, and found out that it was because he wore a wig, and was worried it would come off and embarrass him. As well as causing our PPE enhancement process no end of problems for months, you might be amused to know that even before he'd even left the site, he was widely known as the 'tit with the toupee'. (That's a cleaned-up version – the actual alliteration was on the letter 'w' – as in 'wig'.)

It is fair to say, then, that as well as everything else that went wrong that day, the 'maintaining his dignity' plan didn't work quite the way he'd intended!

The first golden rule, then, is always to follow the rules yourself. (If you find doing so inconvenient, then that's really useful, because so will a lot of other people, and that's a problem that needs proactively addressing. It's a mindset covered in depth in the next chapter.)

Note: as we've said, we are all human, and so we all make mistakes. When we do, we can minimise their impact by the simple 'regret, reason, remedy' approach – essentially, 'I'm sorry, this is why I got this wrong, and this is what I'm going to do about it'. The alternative is get defensive and stroppy and/or pretend it never happened. Research really quite consistently and strongly suggests one of those approaches is better for the creation of a strong and healthy culture than the other!

SETTING THE TONE

I tried to give an example of setting the tone in the preface with some humorous anecdotes. Whilst we're certainly not advocating you start your talk with jokes and funny stories, we *are* advocating that you don't plough straight in to the analytical elements.

It's also worth making the point here that every question we ask and every statement we make contribute to the tone of the organisation. Many organisations make a point of not asking 'why did you switch down?' but instead ask 'why did you think it safe to switch back on?' as the later generates the same technical answer but without the implied 'you'd better have a damn good reason for that' that the former question can suggest. (See, for example, the reluctance of key management on Piper Alpha and Deepwater to take appropriate timely decisions without referring to head office.)

Similarly, organisations like MIND stress that we shouldn't automatically say 'you really have to be able to handle stress to work here' as it suggests it's all about personal resilience. Better, they suggest, to have the mindset 'despite our very best efforts to plan the job, sometimes things can get quite stressful' as this points the organisations mindset at a more holistic and pro-active approach.

Instead, take the time to chat to the person a little, starting with a brief introduction of who you are and what you're doing. This is really important, of course, when we're seeking a 'culture of care'. You might ask:

• How are you? (Initially, this is merely a polite and, frankly, rhetorical question that typically will get a standard 'fine, thank you' answer. But we'll return to this.)

Talk about the weekend's sporting events. Ask after their holiday plans. Anything at all will do, really – just get them talking and at their ease. Time invested in doing this will pay dividends later when you get to the meat of the conversation.

Don't forget that their initial thought will likely be a concern that you are trying to catch them out, so they will most likely be wary of you initially. It's said that a good political interviewer asks themselves, 'Why is this lying git lying to me today?' A variation on this is that initially, we can assume most workers will be asking themselves, 'Why is this nosey git getting in my way and prying into my business?'

Then you can continue on to more practical matters.

- What's it like doing your job nowadays?/How are things going? (Any question at all that moves the conversation towards *task* matters.)

And, of course:

- What are the safety and health implications? (You might want to refer to any risk assessment.)

Applying the 'one minute manager' golden rule of 'catch a person doing something right' is a useful technique to overcome suspicion. However, be sure to do it naturally by picking something that clearly deserves praise, not something that will look trotted out by numbers. For example, 'I'm impressed with the housekeeping – you look very organised' (if they do) is one thing. Looking tongue-tied and, after an uncomfortable silence, blurting out, 'Er . . . you're very, er . . . tall, aren't you . . . well done!?' is quite another.

Again, they are highly likely to want to be rid of you as fast as possible. This is understandable, as no one wants to be interrupted. However, one of the few things we like more than we dislike being interrupted is being asked what we *think* and what we *feel*. If a market researcher whom you try and swerve can stop you and get you talking, then often, you'll be saying 'and you can *write this down too!*' long after their eyes have glazed over, and they've got what they needed (or perhaps that's just me!).

BUILDING TRUST

Studies show that admitting you don't know everything and asking questions increases a person's level of trust in you, rather then reducing their respect. Therefore, since, as previously mentioned, enhancing trust is something that we should all be aiming for within companies, asking questions and listening to the answers is a key component of a good safety and health talk. More than that, it's a key element in building a genuinely caring culture. It's worth restating that wellbeing gurus like Cary Cooper have long claimed that trust levels should be a company's number one metric. (A simple check when in conversation with an employee: is it 'us' and 'we', or 'you', 'I' and 'them'?)

A very well-known culture model is that of the 'Bradley Curve'. This model suggests that we need to move from dependent ('I'll comply but only if you're watching') through 'independent' ('I'll comply even on my own') to, finally, 'interdependent', where we are each our 'brother's keeper'. Interdependence is about trust, teamwork, and all those 'above-the-line behaviours' we discussed previously. A good 'walk and talk' most certainly helps build trust.

Final question. Once *again* . "How *are* you?'

A dedicated health and safety conversation is a perfect place to help build a culture of care, by revisiting that initial 'how are you?' question once a degree of rapport has been established. As we enter a post-Covid world filled with uncertainty and 'long Covid' fatigue, there need be no embarrassment at all in asking it a second time – this time, with meaning. We used to suggest that it be asked if the person looks stressed, or if there's a change in behaviour. On early mental health awareness courses, we'd say, 'Look not just for chatty people who've gone quiet, but for quiet ones who've gone chatty'.

These days, as we emerge from a global shock, just ask it of everyone!

SOME DOS AND DON'TS

The first *don't* is that whilst a safety and health conversation may never be entirely convenient, it's best not to stop someone when it's genuinely inconvenient or even dangerous! *Do* remember to consider whether talking to them now will be a *little* bit inconvenient, or *very* inconvenient.

Do make sure that you *listen*, even if you know the answers already. It's getting them comfortable talking to you that's key here.

Don't ask closed questions if you can avoid it – you'll often get closed answers in response. (Closed questions can be answered with a simple 'yes' or 'no' – open questions ask, for example, 'what do you think?') As I mentioned before, most people will, of course, perfectly reasonably, say 'yes' or 'no' if they can, whether or not that's true, just to get rid of you as quickly as possible.

Do stay professional and *avoid* becoming too 'matey'. Never step beyond friendly and human and into unprofessional. It might make the session pass nicely for you, but you may well not have the impact you want by being 'one of the gang'. It'll also help you avoid saying something that someone finds unacceptable. This is an increasingly serious consideration in these times that are both hugely more enlightened and progressive, but also, at times, perhaps alarmingly oversensitive.

SUMMARY OF KEY POINTS

- Remember that you are *always* leading by example – so you'd best make it positive.
- Remember that whilst there will never be an ideal time and location, some times and locations are better than others!
- Be friendly, but not overly 'matey', and think through the potential unintended consequences of what you genuinely intend to be a non-controversial and endearing *quip*.
- Remember that admitting you don't know everything makes you more trusted.
- Use open, not closed, questions about thoughts and feelings to get people talking.

CHAPTER 4

Analysis

In this chapter I will discuss:

- Human error.
- Just culture.
- Curious whys and 'five whys'.
- ABC analysis.
- The 'anything inconvenient?' technique.

ANALYSIS

The second and, in many respects, most important stage of the conversation is the analysis of any issues seen or raised. This is where the principles of 'just culture' come into play (see Figures 4.1, 4.2, and 4.3). From the world of safety issues, these might include failure to wear PPE, poor housekeeping, driving a forklift truck unsafely, or perhaps a 'toolbox talk' or brief that lacked impact. It also includes poor dialogue generally, pulling the wrong plug out of the wall, and especially poor morale and low levels of engagement. Basically, this includes anything at all we'd rather hadn't happened as, when it comes down to it, almost everything shares the same root cause: people are just people. It's culture and leadership that differ.

So, as we'll see in this chapter, nearly all mistakes occur not because an employee doesn't care, but because they've been set up to fail in some way. And for those few who were set up to succeed and failed because they really couldn't care, well . . . *someone* selected them!

'Just culture' is the model that took the overly simplistic 'no name, no blame' approach forward. (Please see the cartoon a

 DOI: 10.4324/9781003177784-7

Human Failure

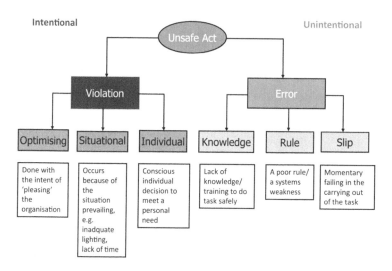

Figure 4.1 'Just culture' model

Source: Adapted from Sidney Dekker, 2012

the front of the book.) Like the Swiss cheese model so often has, the just culture model has been adapted to almost every aspect of human performance and stresses that when we analyse objectively, we'll find that the majority of unwanted acts happen for a reason that makes a certain sense, if you genuinely understand the root cause.

James Reason (who coined the term and did much of his work in aviation) gives a simple example, asking us to consider a worker checking rivets on a plane. He says if the worker has the time, the torch, and the gantry, and does the job conscientiously but misses a few rivets, this is out-and-out human error. Go away and invent a machine that works better than the human eye. If a worker is working conscientiously, but is missing a torch, a gantry, or is under time pressure, then they are blameless, and it's an organisational resource issue. Finally, consider the worker who has the time, the torch, and the gantry, but chooses to work quickly from the ground so they can get back to the canteen and their crossword. This is, he suggests, their fault, and it is *just* that they suffer accordingly.

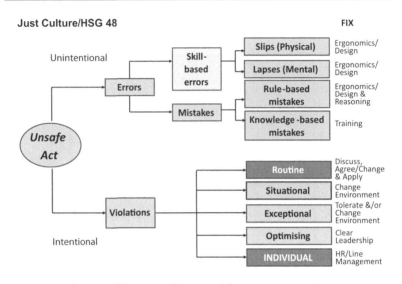

Figure 4.2 Adaption of the 'just culture' model to incorporate HSG/48

Notes: The model above shows the original 'just culture' model adapted to incorporate HSG 48, as many companies prefer. Please note that the addition of an 'exceptional' violation reflects those times when it is adaptive to break the rule. (For example, jumping in the sea from Piper Alpha, which was against training, but which saved many lives.) I have reservations about the inclusion of 'routine' as part of the list of violations. For me, violations that have become routine nearly always commence life as situational ('I had to do it to get the job done') and/or optimising ('I thought that's what you really wanted'). So, I'd prefer the term 'embedded situational'.

Note that only when *all* error and violation options have been investigated and dismissed can we tick the 'individual' box. It's not controversial to suggest that in many organisations, an investigation *starts* with that box as a default.

In truth, only in the minority of cases will a person be off on a folly of their own. The key thing here is to be as analytical and learning-focused as possible, as whatever happens next will be limited by the accuracy of your analysis.

The following is worth stating really bluntly. If you have £100 to spend on safety and health, and 80 per cent of the causes of unsafe acts are physical or cultural, and only 20 per cent are individual, then you need to spend at least £80 on changing the physical and cultural issues. In my experience, many companies get this the wrong way around, and 80 per cent is spent on retraining, inspirational speakers, and the like.

Indeed, Sidney Dekker, in his hugely influential *Field Guide to Understanding Human Error*, would argue that my 80 per cent is actually an underestimate. He also says bluntly:

> *Human error is not the cause, but the effect. Whatever the label (loss of situational awareness, inadequate resources, (even) complacency) human error can never be the conclusion of your investigation. It is the starting point.*

That's worth restating: the efficiency of your response and any use of organisational resources have an upper limit, flukes aside, that is set by the accuracy of your analysis. A couple of quotes from all-time greats:

> *A problem is that if you solved a problem effectively yesterday with a hammer, then tomorrow everything is going to look like a nail. (James Reason)*

> *Always walk for a mile in a man's shoes before you judge them. (Elvis)*

JUST CULTURE

If you follow such influential theories as Reason's 'Swiss cheese' and Dekker's 'just culture' models, you'll find that if you analyse objectively, many unsafe behaviours are out-and-out *unintentional* errors caused by design, task demands, ergonomics, or lack of training ('I don't know what I'm doing and/or I'm physically or mentally incapable of doing it – especially if I'm tired!').

Further, many conscious *violations* (a deliberate breaking of the rules) are often caused by a worker's need to get finished before midnight, and encouraged with 'blind eye' syndrome from those around them! (If this weren't the case, then 'work to rule' wouldn't be such an effective strategy.) It is true that often, an unsafe act is undertaken because the person feels that behaviour was what the company wanted. For example, imagine you do a job well one week and cut a few corners. The only feedback given is 'good job, well done', although management know perfectly well that corners have been cut – or perhaps assume corners must have been cut but 'don't ask so they don't *know*'. This almost guarantees the same corners will be cut again next week. If you wanted to be emotive about it, you could almost call this 'grooming'.

A good question to ask yourself is 'how easily could they do it safely even if they are highly motivated'? – for example if they are being watched by someone in a yellow jacket holding a clipboard. If they really can't, then we need to talk to the training department and/or an ergonomist as soon as possible

To distinguish an *'optimising/situational'* violation from an *'individual'* violation, a more subtle question is *'realistically*, can they do it safely without meaningful inconvenience or discomfort?' Again, if they *can't*, then we, again, need a design solution – unless the discomfort would be entirely social (because it's not custom and practice and they'd stand out from their colleagues). In this case, we need to look squarely at the *cultural* issues.

In the first section, we detailed what a 'mindful' organisation looks like. In doing so, we covered dozens of day-to-day events that cue the workforce to a view of what management 'really, really want' that is a long way from world class. Other examples of 'productivity before welfare' cues would include having a safety moment as the first item on an agenda (as required), but addressing it in a way that makes it clear we are to get through it as fast as possible so that we can crack on with the *important* stuff.

The core of a 'just culture', then, is to step back and apply some objective analysis before rushing to judgement. Just asking 'why?' of an unwanted event in a genuinely *curious* manner will pretty much do it. If you ask it curiously, you'll find that in 80 to 90 per cent of cases, you'll learn something interesting, even if it's just that there's a systemic *temptation* to cut a corner. ('Five whys' is the simple but powerful technique of continuing to ask the question why of the initial answers and reflects the fact that you'll get to the root cause in no more than five steps).

Engagement. Adopting a 'just culture' approach simply can't be done well without talking with, and listening to, the workforce. They're the experts about what happens and why, after all. It has an additional benefit too. Research shows clearly that the more 'just' the culture is perceived to be, the more effective the *basic* and *reactive* incident reporting and analysis system, because employees will more readily engage and disclose. It also impacts well on spurious claims, turnover, absenteeism, 'presenteeism', and general motivation.

I'd like to strongly suggest, therefore, that talking about transformational safety leadership without explicit reference to 'just culture' and 'why?' analysis is, to me, really missing the most important trick. 'Catching someone doing something right' is great. Coaching them when catching them doing something wrong is also best practise. Neither comes close to beating learning-based dialogue.

The legendary Irish rugby player Willie John McBride, who captained the British Lions to an unbeaten tour of South Africa in 1974, is certainly one of the most inspirational rugby captains ever. The diminutive Welsh legend Phil Bennet says McBride 'always made him feel seven feet tall'. However, though his role was vital, all objective analyses of the series acknowledge that the ground-breaking coaching and preparation the squad received were probably far more important. An awful lot of thought, analysis, and preparation preceded anyone lacing a pair of boots and psyching themselves up in the changing room before the match.

On the other hand, although it's *analysis* that gives any human factor process its real 'engine', it must be said that 'transformational' leadership behaviour, as discussed in Section One, is also vital. It really didn't hurt that Bennet would 'run through a wall for McBride'. The two are interlinked and self-supporting.

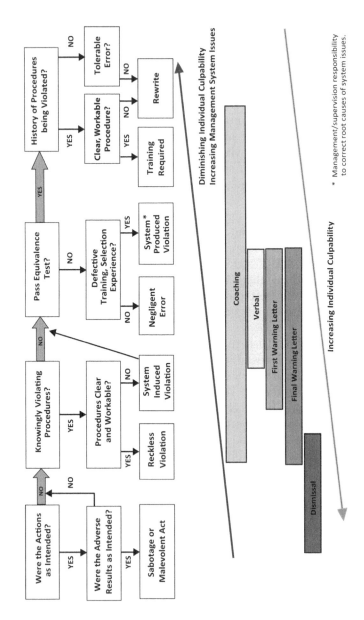

Figure 4.3 Just culture example

When a workforce is asked to describe the traits of the best safety leader they have seen – one they would trust to keep their children safe – they always include 'trustworthy, consistent, transparent, and fair'. Taking the basic analytical model above (Figure S2 4.3), and validating it with the workforce before systematically rolling it out through human resources, is a very good way of helping increase these traits in frontline management.

ANALYTICAL METHODOLOGIES: THE 'CURIOUS WHY'

If a company can double the number of times managers ask the question 'why' with *curiosity* – and, of course, do something with the answers – then the culture will be transformed. I guarantee it. Importantly, it's very much worth stressing that the 'why' question *must be* asked with a *curious* tone. Ask it aggressively, and the person you are talking to will very likely get defensive and clam up.

Even if the answer to this question shows that it *is* the person who is at fault, you still learn something. If what you learn is that the person you're talking to is indeed 'bang to rights', then a more *robust* response is appropriate. That would be the justice in 'just culture'. As above, it's not easy when you really analyse in depth, however, to come up with a good example of someone who is genuinely 'guilty, pure and simple'.

Let's return to the rivet checker (above), and three more examples I've genuinely come across on my travels, where 'guilt' looks clear cut.

- (As discussed previously) a worker checks rivets quickly from the ground, so they can get back to the canteen and finish their crossword.
- We find a group of workers indulging in a game of darts inside a factory with air-powered nail guns. (On a Friday afternoon, they have an organised forklift truck grand prix.)
- We find a worker walking around a factory with a hole poked in their face mask so they can have a cigarette from time to time.

- A worker has their mandatory safety glasses on, but has poked the glass out.

Pretty clear-cut? Not in any of the cases, actually; by applying the Elvis rule of walking a mile in their shoes before we judge them, we find that:

The rivet checker: it turns out that this worker had been doing this job without break or rotation for more than a year. She was bored senseless, and had never been certain exactly what she was looking for, as her initial training was inadequate. When she first started nipping off early, her supervisor saw her and said nothing. (Indeed, that would have been a bit hypocritical, as he did the same when he stood in.)

The dart players and racers: for years, this was considered a perk of doing a 'real man's job', and nearly every manager and supervisor in the place had been involved in these games when they were younger and less senior. Indeed, the new owner's utter mortification at coming across these games was met with genuine incredulity by the workers.

The smoker: they had never pulled up on it before the safety inspection, despite being seen hundreds of times over the years by managers, who were doing it themselves when the worker first joined the company. They thought no one would see from a distance, and since it's only a small hole, they were still largely protected from fumes. Re-using this – real! – smoking (& smoking *inside*) example reminds me just how long I've been involved in the game!

Missing lenses: this worker was genuinely convinced by the widely believed rumour that the plastic lenses would damage his already failing eyesight. He was really vain, couldn't stand the thought of contacts, and didn't want to wear glasses.

The good news is that by being systematically analytical first, any 'justice' is both less frequent and transparently fairer when it is required. This in itself helps move the whole company culture forward.

As intimated, the trick is to then *do* something with all this learning, which many organisations find difficult, though not all. For example, at the 2011 IOSH rail conference, East Midland Trains produced some graphs showing impressive improvements in incident rates, and made the comment:

> *For us, the key was to stop treating SPADs (signals passed at danger) as events in themselves, but as symptoms of a more underlying issue. That shift in mindset was vital.*

This is where we came in, when we discussed hitting diminishing returns with systems and procedures. It's that shift in mindset that is so often vital.

A PROACTIVE METHODOLOGY: THE HYPOTHETICAL 'ANYTHING SLOW OR UNCOMFORTABLE?' TEMPTATION QUESTION

If no issues have been raised by the initial observation, then the person running the safety contact needs to start a hypothetical discussion. There will always be something to be discussed, and the question, 'Anything slow or uncomfortable about doing this job or task in a safe or healthy way?' will nearly *always* raise some issues.

The good news is that, compared to 'curious why', it's even easier to transform a culture by doubling the number of times a manager asks a hypothetical question, because in most companies, it's simply not being asked *at all*.

THE POWER OF TEMPTATION

Oscar Wilde quipped that he could 'resist everything except temptation'. The UK comedian Stephen Fry explains that he 'always gives in to temptation straight away – it saves me lots of time'. We find these quips amusing because we recognise the psychology behind them, and this psychology most directly answers the question we are most frequently asked as psychologists: 'Why *do* people do the risky things they do?'

SOME EXAMPLES OF THE POWER OF TEMPTATION

Earlier in the century, almost half the UK's MPs had to pay back expenses, having given in to the temptation of over-claiming expenses. (Interestingly, many new MPs who resisted over-claiming initially gave testimony that they came under pressure from the old hands not to 'make them look bad', a classic example of the pervasiveness of existing culture to prompt 'bad' behaviour.)

It's also said that the financial crisis of 2008 was triggered by the abundance of cheap credit available in the years leading up to it. To quote Michael Lewis in *The Sunday Times:*

> The tidal wave of cheap money that rolled across the planet between 2002 and 2007 wasn't just money, it was temptation. It offered entire societies the chance to reveal aspects of themselves they could normally not afford to indulge. Entire countries were told 'the lights are out, you can do what you want in the dark' . . . Americans wanted to own homes larger than they could afford, Icelanders wanted to stop fishing and become investment bankers, and the Greeks wanted to be treated as a properly functioning northern European economy but whilst carrying on with an inefficient and corrupt culture but . . . with access to cheap loans.

This isn't an individual issue – it's a *species* issue.

Every few months famous someone is found to have 'done an Oscar Wilde' and given in to temptation: evangelical preachers in the United States, or British Prime Ministers in the middle of 'back to basics morals' crusades. Perhaps the best play I've seen in the last decade is *People, Places, Things*, a jet-black comedy about overcoming addiction. The title of the play refers to the vital importance of changing the environment so as to avoid being triggered to previous behaviour. Studies of addiction show that some people can go back to their old environment and change behaviour just through willpower alone – not very many, though.

What these mainstream examples show is that it is true that we find temptation difficult to resist, and the implications for safety and health are enormous.

At this point we really need to talk about ABC analysis.

ABC ANALYSIS

ABC analysis shows us that even where the long-term consequences of behaviour can be very important, it's the short-term consequences that mostly determine whether someone behaves in this way. ABC stands for *antecedents, behaviours,* and *consequences. Antecedents* means all triggers, such as training and signage, and anything contextual that's relevant – such as the fact that the person is tired, badly equipped, badly trained, or 'struggling' in some way.

So, for example, we smoke and drink and eat rich food and skip the gym and hope for the best regarding illnesses such as heart disease and cancer, and we speed in our cars to save time even though we know driving is by far the most dangerous thing we'll ever do. We flop in front of the TV and say, 'I just need 10 minutes', then take an hour when the people most precious to us desperately need to talk to us.

This principle is important at work, as when the safe or healthy way is slow, uncomfortable, or inconvenient, we are tempted to cut the corner and 'crack on'. And, of course, we nearly always get away with it, which is rewarding and validates our instinctive 'dynamic risk assessment'. However, as explained in Section One, the laws of Heinrich's Principle tell us that some of the corner-cutters will inevitably get hurt or ill sooner or later. In the case of pathogen-triggered illness, the consequences may be severe, with a conservative estimate of a hundred deaths to exposure to toxins for every one death to an incident, but this will be decades later, with all the legislators and c-suite long retired. (Therefore, it's impossible to overstate its importance, but it's largely beyond the direct scope of this book. Not entirely, though, and I touch on it briefly in the following passages).

I'd therefore argue that where there is a temptation to cut a corner because the safe or healthy way is slow or inconvenient in some way, this temptation is as systemic a risk as an unguarded drop or unguarded piece of machinery. Because people are people and not robots, unsafe behaviour in these circumstances merely reflect human nature, and it's just a question of how soon someone gets hurt.

We can, therefore, wait until an incident and find out about these temptations from a (good) accident investigation, then exhort our workers not to give in to such temptations (a thankless task) – or we can proactively get out and about and discover these temptations and, whenever practicable, *design them out* of the workplace.

We can also get creative and put designs in place that help our situational awareness. It's very difficult to worry about airborne particles that we can't see, and the BOHS (British Occupational Hygiene Society) has long pioneered the use of ultraviolet lighting to show what we're actually breathing in. (Covid campaigns are using the same tactic as I write.)

USING THE INFORMATION

As with a 'why' analysis, any suggestion for improvements that are agreed to be 'high impact, low cost' should be invested in as soon as possible. In addition, the people who came up with the analysis should be lavished with praise, both personally and through in-house media such as newsletters. (We will talk more about the importance of praise in Chapter 5, on coaching.) In addition, of course, the organisation should share and disseminate this best practice as widely as it can. 'Not invented here' syndrome might well kick in – but not in organisations where adopting others' good ideas is a tracked metric, because there's nearly always a way of nudging and rewarding what we want.

We are very good at spotting mistakes – it's hard wired into us as people – but we are less good at spotting safe or healthy behaviour. Consider the contents of *any* newspaper or TV news programme, and how you'd feel if someone asked to 'talk to you about your behaviour'. Ominous, no matter what their tone of voice! Blame comes naturally to us.

Even more motivating than praise is the simple act of listening to someone, and then acting on anything sensible they say. We all enjoy warm words, but actually *applying* someone's knowledge and experience is, like imitation, as sincere as praise can get. The individual will be certain to feel valued and useful.

SUMMARY OF KEY POINTS

Finally, as a reminder of the points discussed in this chapter, here's a checklist of questions to ask the workforce, the answers to which might help you understand what's really going on:

- Why did you do that?/Does this happen? ('Why' should be asked *curiously*.)
- Is there anything slow, uncomfortable, or inconvenient about doing this job safely?
- I want you to work in a safe and healthy manner, as well as a productive one. I'm sure you want the same. What do you need from me to do that?
- Ask yourself, '*Can* they do it safely if their lives depended on it?'
- Ask, '*Realistically*, can they do it safely without meaningful inconvenience or discomfort?' (Including norm-based psychological discomfort.)

Other questions worth asking yourself (or the person being talked to, if they trust you enough to answer):

- How often does this unsafe act occur?
- How many do it?
- Has it ever been seen by a supervisor and, if so, what did they do when they saw it?
- What did they do when they saw it done safely?
- What do peers say if they see it?

TRAINING FOLLOW UP TO EMBED
SAFE WORKING

The learning opportunities that flow from these question lists are boundless and self-evident. Training supervisors *how* to ask them and *why* isn't difficult. However, I do stress that, as above, that's only 20 per cent of the culture change. The organisation really must, some months later, invest quality time in asking the workforce how often these questions have been asked of them – and how skilfully – to track and drive the other 80 per cent benefit.

CHAPTER 5
Coaching

In this chapter, I will discuss:

- The basics of coaching: the 'feedback fish'.
- Ownership and involvement.
- Reward and praise.
- Listening.
- Data and illustration.
- Assertion – always 'middle bubble', please!

The first thing to note is that you may not need to coach at all, as you'll have covered many of the key elements of culture creation when analysing.

But after analysis, the coaching element of the safety contact is the second key element of the 'inspirational' leadership behaviours we discussed at the start of the book. Certainly, it's often said that the worst way to get a person to do something is to tell them to do it, and this seems true of the typical western worker in particular.

Developing a good style is important to coaching, as if you are at all threatening or annoying, then they'll not want to work with you. When you want to consider classic coaching questions like 'What if this happens?' scenarios, for example, they'll be thinking not, 'What's the worst that could happen?' as you're encouraging, but 'Who the hell are you?' (Or worse!) Therefore, as previously discussed, first you need to introduce yourself, break the ice, put them at ease, and avoid confrontation best as possible.

Sometimes, however, the person you are talking to may be defensive, provocative, or incorrect, but you should strive to

DOI: 10.4324/9781003177784-8

avoid taking them on and/or 'putting them right'. (Unless, of course, that's unavoidable or appropriate – after all, although we're advocating that a good safety and health guerrilla fighter is, first and foremost, clever and thoughtful, they do need to strike decisively at times.) Use techniques like the 'flat bat' neutral paraphrase to confirm you're listening, even if you don't necessarily agree. For example: 'So what you're saying is that all management are paper-pushing Muppets who haven't done a proper day's work in their lives, and therefore know nothing about your day-to-day realities?' (Ideally, followed by 'OK, that's a view you obviously feel passionate about. So, what do we need to do better?')

Remember, when people decide of their own volition to do something, then there's no stopping them. I like the lesson of the Scottish football fans, who began behaving really well at foreign tournaments after being praised for their good-natured party with Brazilian fans following a narrow but rather glorious defeat in a World Cup. The headlines were 'Scots in big party with Brazilians after heroic exit – hardly any arrests. (What a contrast with the English!)' Since then, Scottish fans have made huge efforts to show up the English. A number of infamous incidents prior to this Brazilian match, in places like Rotterdam and London, illustrate just how dramatic the improvement has been. (This is also illustrated by continuing issues at domestic matches.)

Ironically, Manchester Council were very well aware of this mindset and reputation when they naively invited half of Glasgow along to party and spend their money in its bars at the UEFA cup final of 2008. The council were complacent and didn't make proper provisions, leading the fans to feel, probably quite accurately, that it was only their money the council were interested in. The subsequent behaviour proved an exception to the rule, as well as an example of how quickly trust can be lost.

Coaching, with its emphasis on discussion, thought, and interaction, is much more likely to induce a light-bulb 'oh, I see! Right then' learning moment than a directive 'do as I say' style. This is important, as we want all employees to fully understand the reasoning behind the rule or request, so that later they can accurately risk assess going forward. We want them to automatically ask the question 'what if?' Therefore, as well as thinking and planning, there's also an important motivational and embedding element here.

Behavioural scientists stress that the future is more emotionally motivating precisely because it hasn't happened yet. There's the energising possibility of *control*. Uncertainty is exciting, if sometimes frightening. We can't change the past, but we can, and do, often rationalise our mistakes. When we look back, we can see clearly that the mistakes of the past weren't entirely our fault, and we certainly won't be repeating those mistakes in the future! That's perfectly natural for ego protection, but it hinders learning. When we plan to run a half marathon for charity, we get excited about what we are going to do and how great it will be, often dismissing the valuable learning points from the five times we signed up in the past and failed to even make the start line. But when we really commit to a target, like running that 'fun' 10k in less than an hour, we'll risk a heart attack in the last 200 metres to achieve it. (Even though not even our families care a jot whether our time is 59 mins something, or 60 mins something.)

The good news is that discussing the *future* is 'pushing on an open door'. President Obama used this rather well with his positive, vague, but highly successful 'yes we can!' slogan. A good coach simply needs to add some detail and planning to that optimism and positivity!

I remember setting up my consultancy back in the early 1990s. The adrenalin rush of early clients and planning with optimism isn't something I've come close to matching, even though the consultancy was far more successful than I'd even hoped. 'Another client! That's three now, three! Carry on like this, and by the end of next year we might even have ten!'

This motivation from genuine ownership can frequently be seen. A few years ago, for example, I tried to calm the nerves of the 55-year-old chair of a shop floor volunteer team we'd set up, who was waiting to present some improvement ideas to the board of the company he worked for. His 'calming' drink had turned into *several* calming drinks. Luckily, his adrenalin levels were so high that the alcohol wasn't affecting him, but he said something very interesting: 'I've never been this nervous about anything before . . . but it's great, really. I'm loving this', and then added something hugely meaningful for the messages in this book: 'You know, in 30 years with this company, this is the first time I've taken any work home . . . there's a thing, eh?!' (When I left the hotel later, I noticed he was back at the bar, but this time in the company of the German CEO. They were getting on like a house on fire. Sometimes my job is hugely rewarding.)

The following section looks at some basic techniques for ensuring the coaching element of the safety talk goes well, and that some 'ownership' of the future is generated. In essence, this whole section is about facilitating the workforce to be *active* rather than passive in their thinking and behaviour.

COACHING BASICS: THE 'FEEDBACK FISH'

Many supervisors have never been taught basic techniques for coaching. However, if you understand the principle of the 'feedback fish', you'll understand the basics of coaching. Imagine your five-year-old has brought you a picture of a fish, and it's pretty rubbish – just a rough outline with no detail (Figure 5.1). You'd be unlikely to say, 'That's crap that! Looks more like a biscuit'. Instead, you'd probably compliment its brilliance, then hint about things that would improve it, by asking questions such as, 'Let me think – how do fish see?' and the five-year-old will shout, 'Eyes!' and draw one in (Figure 5.2).

Figure 5.1 The feedback fish (first attempt)

Figure 5.2 The feedback fish (second attempt)

Though the fish is a simple, even childish, example, the analogy is very apt. Studies show that for ownership of a solution or idea to kick in, the key thing seems to be that the person being coached is the one that *says the answer first out loud*. This is true even if both people talking know full well that the 'coach' knew the answer and led them to it with questions. Of course, as with everything else in this section, using a questioning technique rather than telling is a key component of good leadership *in general*. Indeed, the major principles are all generic. The most powerful coaching techniques have just as direct a relevance for safety and health management as they do for a management or leadership role.

When visiting a peripatetic road gang, a manager might point out that they are unloading the van and setting up but haven't erected barriers.

'What *are* you doing?! Where are the bloody barriers!?'

Alternatively, he can start a conversation about the order in which the job should be set up as per the risk assessment. What's key is that the worker has the opportunity to say something like, 'Ah, that reminds me: we're cracked on with the job here before we put the barriers up. Better put that right *straight away*!'

It takes a little more time, but to try and model the technique itself here, I'll ask the following genuine question: which approach do you think will be most likely to impact the workers' behaviour in the future? Especially when there's very little chance of a visit?

OWNERSHIP AND INVOLVEMENT

We mentioned the saying in Section One, 'My idea had better be four times better than yours before I'll impose it on you, as I know you'll work three times harder on your own idea than you will on mine'. The quality guru Deming said, 'A person most owns what they helped create'. Inevitably, where the workforce has a good level of ownership of safety and health, the culture will be strong. I don't think I've ever seen a single example that contradicts this rule.

To a busy manager, ownership and involvement can look very similar at a glance, but in practice, they aren't at all. Involvement implies asking the 'usual suspects' to ratify or comment on a decision already provisionally taken by management. (A better version of involvement is having them be a part of the team that takes the decision, but it will almost certainly still involve the 'usual suspects'.) The problem is that whilst this process has input from the serial volunteer and naturally positive 'usual suspects', it's rarely these individuals we are seeking to influence.

Ownership involves giving the workforce itself a blank piece of paper and asking 'what do *you think?*'

The analogy I personally best like is a rugby one. The difference between ownership and involvement is like being involved in a scrum in the middle of a rugby pitch. Whether the scrum is inching forwards or inching backwards looks much the same from the stands – just 16 large men pushing each other over the ball. However, if you're the No. 8 at the back of the scrum, or the scrum half *on the pitch* who have to do something with the ball, it can make all the difference in the world. Even world-class players can look like very ordinary ones when starting to attack whilst inching backwards.

Inching backwards – there's 'nudge' again, and this absolutely reflects how nudge theory and management commitment interact. Asking 'what do *you* think?' requires more time and effort than asking 'any problems with what *I* think?', but that effort can make a huge difference to the safety and health culture. And, as we've said, it's true that we build a culture one bit of effort, one conversation at a time.

But some effort is far better targeted and far more productive than others

REWARD AND PRAISE: THE POWER OF POSITIVE REINFORCEMENT

It's suggested that praise is something like ten to 20 times as effective in changing a person's behaviour as criticism. This is because (as in Section One) we are all hard-wired to be optimistic, overconfident, and to learn from positive experiences. The parts of our brain that deal with positive experiences are more sensitive and powerful than the negative.

One of the very best-selling management textbooks of all time, *The One Minute Manager*, includes the key slogan 'catch a person doing something *right*'. Indeed, it's a key element of all 'how-to' texts, including *The Seven Habits of Highly Effective People*.

In order for criticism to resonate, and not be seen as yet another nag, it needs to have been preceded by three praises, ideally. This 3:1 ratio is quoted on just about every management course. Imagine being told a month prior to an appraisal, 'Those two areas of weakness we discussed last year – I've noticed a significant improvement over the last 11 months, and am really looking forward to giving you that feedback formally next month'. What ratio of criticism would match the increase in motivation? Would it even be possible?

An interesting spot check is to ask a workforce how many instances of praise they get relative to criticism. It isn't ever 1:3 that's for sure! Indeed, when doing our culture surveys, we have a scale that ranges from 'uncontrollable derisory laughter' all the way through to 'no, that's not true, *never* isn't fair. I was praised once last year, I think!' I exaggerate, of course, but it's true that few management teams have maximised their opportunities here.

A manager needs to have a default setting as the encouraging and praising coach. That way, when they do need to give some negative feedback, it is far more likely to be listened to and be impactful. It's very difficult to feel that you've let someone down when their default setting is to criticise all the time and, frankly, even when you know you *have* let them down, it's difficult to care!

A word of warning is required here. Some cultures find giving praise harder than others. For example, some US 'how to praise' videos really don't travel very well, especially to countries where a significant minority of the workforce can be *unhealthily* negative and cynical, with the rest having a healthy scepticism. (I've tried to have some fun with a couple of cartoons in the book and capture the real facial expressions I've often seen.)

Many training materials and techniques that work in one culture may well backfire in another. The way that praise is given is a prime example.

PRAISING THE CYNICAL WORKER

Luckily, there are several robust techniques that can be used with even the most cynical worker. One really useful example is called the 'one in ten' technique, which can be used for anything, and especially any wellbeing issue. Now, I know the idea of frontline managers actually coaching wellbeing issues, like sleep, diet, or exercise on a regular basis, may sound like I'm pushing it a little, to put it mildly. But that said, as we talk about mental health more and more, comments like 'I'm not sleeping well' or 'if only I could get a good night's sleep' will be heard more often. Frankly, proactively asking about elements of a person's wellbeing and then using this technique should be standard.

The technique involves asking someone to rate themselves on a task from one (poor) to ten (good). When they respond with seven, perhaps don't ask, 'Why only a seven!?', but instead respond, 'Excellent, but can I ask why you aren't a ten? What do you do well?' When they explain why they rated themselves a seven, you listen, nod, smile, murmur, and maybe even say 'sounds more like an eight to me!' When you have built some rapport and offered some praise naturally for what they actually do well, you switch to coaching mode by asking:

> But you know, with my wellbeing hat on, I'd like to halve problems. So, if I can get you up from that eight to a nine, that's my job done – well, for now, at least. How do you think we could do that?

I'm sure you can imagine the two people are now well primed to have a productive and constructive chat. Particularly so, as this approach nearly always leads naturally to 'curious why' questions and the other empathic objective analysis techniques that we keep stressing as vital. A few years ago, the head of safety of a company using this exact approach told me:

> The other day I walked past a real old-school head banger (UK speak for a problematic and/or foolish individual!) . . . and he was actually having a constructive safety chat with one of our team. I tell you, I thought 'well, I'll be *&Λ%!!'

Since this chap runs a shipbuilding yard, I'll argue if they can use it well, *anyone* can. Indeed, it transpired that their 11 safety reps undertaking three 'one in ten' talks a week was their *entire* and *award-winning* behavioural safety process. I talked to them about the other steps described here, but they said, 'But all the other "why?" stuff flows naturally from a good one in ten chat anyway'.

The important point is that one of the problems we constantly face is this: we're asked to do something that is apparently sensible and effective, but because it comes straight from a textbook (or an HQ in a different country), it isn't *appropriate* locally in its original format, and it goes down like a lead balloon.

More positively, I've seen plenty of examples of material being adjusted successfully to be culturally specific, such as key learning from the Koran being used in the Middle East to back up training points – or a delivery style that reflects that Antipodeans tend to like their messages as direct as possible. ('No dickheads', remember?). I don't have the space – or the knowledge – to suggest a list of adjustments, and indeed, you may need to think as much about the culture of your specific organisation as about the national culture when designing a programme.

One of the most famous speeches of all time, Dr Martin Luther King's 'I Have a Dream' speech, is an excellent example of learning from feedback and showing flexibility, as well as inspirational leadership. The key words we all remember weren't actually in the formal draft, and his speech was, apparently, a bit leaden until an aide tapped his arm and whispered, 'Why not try that "dream" stuff that went down so well in the church the other day?'

So, some lessons on *listening* to the people around us are in there too!

There's an important generic lesson from the shipyard example, and that is that we mustn't give up on a sound but rather tricky principle – in this case praise – just because of early setbacks. We must be flexible and persistent and find a better, more appropriate, way of applying it locally.

LISTENING

It's worth considering 'listening' skills formally for two reasons already considered in previous passages. One, because you might learn something, of course. Two, because it also helps empower the person you're listening to. Here, I'd like to quote perhaps the most revered modern leader of them all to connect listening, learning, and leading together, using the following famous example.

When locked up on Robben Island, Nelson Mandela would make a point of spending as much time as possible talking to his guards. Not just because he was trying to convert South Africa one person at a time – though of course he was – but because:

> *In genuinely listening to them I learned so much about the Boer mind-set. Their values, hopes and fears. It stood me in such good stead later when we opened formal negotiations. I had more understanding and more respect.*

And to address the second point directly – that you can influence the person you listen to by the very act of listening – we all know just how many of these guards were later in attendance at his presidential inauguration, shedding tears of joy. (As shown in the film *Invictus*, his was a lone voice when the ANC debated taking the famous green and gold jersey off the rugby team. 'It means so much to them we should let them keep it', he suggested. As the film and history shows, he wasn't wrong, and that insight came from talking to his rugby-mad guards).

The basic technique is simple:

- Pay full attention to their words, and to their body language and tone. (Don't just rehearse what you're going to say next whilst you wait for them to stop talking!)
- Reflect back facts to check simple messages.
- Reflect back feelings with a paraphrase (not just the same words) to confirm understanding, unless it's not just fact based.

We all find these simple rules easier to agree with than to undertake, but remember the old saying: 'Two eyes, two ears, just the one mouth. Work that ratio!'

THE USE OF 'RATIONAL DATA' AND ILLUSTRATION

I have saved one of the best coaching techniques until last.

The numerous studies of leadership and coaching suggests that perhaps the single most effective way of changing a person's behaviour is through the use of rational data, ideally backed up with some memorable illustration. For example, we discussed the likelihood of falling down the stairs in the first chapter. For what it's worth, about half of all lost time injuries (LTIs) in the offshore industry are caused by falling down the stairs (at a cost of tens of millions of pounds), but the probability of a fall is only around 100,000:1. This means that if a person who never holds the handrail gets lucky, they might go an entire career without falling – and a supervisor has a good excuse for not making a challenge (after all, a fall is unlikely on any given day, and asking someone to do something as apparently mundane as holding the handrail may lead to a scornful response).

However, imagine the following conversation:

> I've just been on a course about behavioural safety, and did you know that 50 per cent of all lost time injuries out here are falling down the stairs? Costs the industry about £12m annually, apparently. I wonder how many jobs that represents in the current climate?

(Pause.)

> Only I noticed you weren't . . .

I'm sure you can imagine a conversation which would be much more likely to go well from here. (I did only say 'more likely'!) The reason is simple – absolutely *no one* likes to be wrong, but most of us are happy to admit that we don't know everything and are comfortable about being uninformed. (I did say *most* of us.)

TERRORISM AND SEAT BELTS

On courses, I like to ask how many people have recently challenged a taxi driver for not wearing his or her seat belt. It will be few if any who raise their hands.

We then discuss just how dangerous the roads are, with reference to terrorism attacks as a benchmark. The facts are that since the attacks of 9/11, less than 2,000 people have been killed by terrorists worldwide (as of 2021), but around 24 million have been killed in car accidents. (The fatal road accident rate is around 1.2 million a year.) Indeed, a famous example of the law of unintended consequences that links the two issues is that, the year after 9/11, an *additional* 3,000 people were killed on the roads of America compared to an average year, because so many people switched from air travel to the much more dangerous roads.

We then talk specifically about how many people are killed by drivers who roll their cars and end up in the back seat. Worse, when a driver is thrown about in a rolling car, it's always the diagonal seat they end up in, which is where most of us sit in taxis so as not to appear rude. (Sitting directly behind the driver suggests we have no intention of talking to them, so we don't often do that, even if we have absolutely no intention of talking to them!)

Of that 1.2 million, about 30,000 worldwide are killed as a consequence of being hit by a fellow passenger being flung around. This makes an un-buckled taxi driver around 330 times more dangerous to you than a terrorist (statistically speaking). At this point, we show an in-cab clip of a driver rolling his car and ending up in the back seat with some force. Even at 30mph (as in the clip), it makes for pretty loud and spectacular viewing, though it's always worth pointing out that at 60mph, he'd go back with four times as much force.

We then ask the audience if they will be more likely to say something next time they get in a taxi and notice the driver is unbuckled, and most hands go up. (Feedback from former delegates suggests that around 50 per cent do then challenge the next driver about the seat belt. I've noticed that the majority of those who admit they didn't ask *do* at least look uncomfortable about it, so at least they're now clearly more 'mindful' of the risk.)

The message is simple: explain your reasoning with the use of rational data, and illustrate it memorably if you can. It will maximise the chance of change.

A PERSONAL TESTIMONY – AND 'MICRO-MORTS'

In 2010, just after the Christmas break, I needed to visit a potential client in deepest British countryside in Norfolk, and chose to travel there by train.

During the visit, I discussed my travel options with the CEO, and he asked me why I'd not driven. I explained that my decision had been influenced my knowledge of 'micro-morts'. A 'micro-mort' is basically a one in a million chance of dying in an accident. (For example, it's every 6,000 miles in a train, 230 miles on a road, six on a motorbike – 180 yards on a motorbike if over the alcohol limit! – and so on.)

I explained I'd been up late all holiday watching the cricket in Australia, and the return to work was a bit of a shock. This meant that whilst the early hours of the journey should be OK, as it was on a motorway, during the final two hours of driving, fatigue would likely have been setting in, at pub closing time, in the dark, on Norfolk's somewhat notorious 'A' roads. Now although I'm not particularly risk averse, I'd realised my micro-mort rating would go through the roof. It's worth noting that the actual risk level remained pretty good – it was the *increase* in relative risk that made me wince.

He responded that many people had told him over the years they'd considered taking the train to visit the company for that very reason, but then hadn't actually done so. The exception was one chap – their advanced driver coach – who apparently *always* takes the train to them! So, I like to think this is a good example of user-friendly rational data helping you think like the professionals!

Let me square this whole positive feedback, 'coaching' techniques circle entirely. When this (at that time, only a *potential* client) said 'Hmm, I'm impressed to see that you walk the talk!', what do you think it did to my likelihood of catching the train again next time?

ASSERTION – 'BUBBLES THEORY'

Finally, I'd like to suggest a mindset that can help *all* interactions go well. This technique takes advantage of the fact that we can't think and react instinctively at the same time. It has its basis in work in Transactional Analysis Interpersonal theory, which came out of California in the 1960s. (Don't be put off by the fact that we've had clients from the building and road construction industries brand their entire cultural training programme 'bubbles training').

The basic model is like a snowman (see Figure 5.3), with three bubbles on top of each other. The lower bubble represents passive, sulking behaviour. The top bubble represents aggressive, authoritarian, or paternal behaviour. The middle bubble, however, is where you ought to be – firm, fair, *analytical*, and reasonable behaviours.

You'll find that when you stop, step back, and analyse yourself, you'll be amazed how often you *don't* qualify for middle bubble status. Some examples:

> *Consider first the manager (as previously mentioned) who closes a meeting with a challenging, 'So we're all agreed? Anyone got a problem with that? No? Good! Let's go then!' This is delivered from a standing position, leaning on the desk, with entirely rhetorical body language and tone of voice. We all know that when things go wrong, this person* isn't *going to say, 'Well, it was all my decision, given my tone of voice and body language and the way I didn't give anyone a chance to respond. I mean, I effectively made it impossible for anyone to object, didn't I?'*

The theory also talks of the 'nurturing parent'. This is still 'top bubble', but without the aggression. The trouble is that your paternal attitude may well be seen as patronising (because it is, as you're talking down to people). This mindset will inhibit other people's development and growth, and will get in the way of your listening and communication skills, as you're assuming you know best. Again, a strong culture needs to be based on genuine listening, learning, and mutual respect.

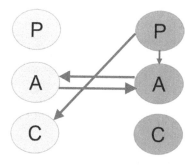

Figure 5.3 Transactional analysis – parent, adult, or child?

For example, if you've ever said to someone, 'Can I give you some *advice?*', even in a kindly way, you will have found that they rarely say, 'Yes please!', but rather automatically respond with, 'No – you can bugger off!' or maybe just, 'Would you mind if you didn't?'. If they listen at all, it will probably be grudgingly, even when the advice was actually really useful.

WHY 'BUBBLES' WORKS

There are two key factors to consider. First, as above, *thinking* and *reacting* are mutually exclusive, so if you can train yourself to stop and *think* which of the three bubbles you are in, then you're halfway there already. The second thing is to remember that behaviour breeds behaviour, so if you're in your middle bubble, other people will tend to match that. Sometimes it takes a little patience, of course, but it will happen more often than not. On the flip side, if you're *not* in your middle bubble, it's really not very easy for people around you to be in theirs, because *behaviour breeds behaviour*. Aggressive responses generate aggression, and sulking but pleasant objective responses usually generate similar.

The real problem is that not being in the middle bubble nearly *always* leads to problems later. Being passive means you avoid confrontation, but also means people will take advantage, you'll lose respect, and you will probably feel weak. Being aggressive means you might get what you want in the short term, but people will resent you, and almost certainly strive to 'get you back' in some way later.

For example, I ran a course in Romania for a shipping company some years ago, and we discussed how this might work. We filled a flip chart with terms such as 'withholding information', 'not helping new starts', 'boycotting social events', 'working slowly', 'looking to leave the company', 'criticising the company in a bar', and so on. At the end of this session, one young officer pointed to a scar on her ear and observed: 'Or losing your head – *literally!*'

Her story was that a few months before, she'd been examining a valve that had blown off and nearly taken her head with it cutting her ear as it went. Basically, someone they never caught had sabotaged the valve, and it turned out there was a lot of bad feeling on the ship because of some very aggressive criticism that had been given to the whole crew some days before.

SUMMARY OF KEY POINTS

Finally, as a reminder of the points above here's a checklist of questions to ask the workforce, the answers to which might really help you understand how well the workforce are coached for health and safety:

- Ask when the last time someone walked them through a 'what if?' situation seeking to draw out their knowledge, rather than simply tell them what to do.
- Ask when they were last praised for a safe act or healthy choice.
- Ask if that praise was given in a way that seemed genuine.
- We can ask when the last time someone explained 'why' to them in a way that made logical sense – whether it be about a work change, a rule, or some such.
- Ask, did they use logical data? Did they try and illustrate the point with something memorable?
- Ask, how many communications are 'middle bubble' to 'middle bubble'?

CHAPTER 6

Eliciting a promise (?)

In this short chapter that is really only about short-term safety, I will discuss:

- The power of eyes and the word 'I'.
- Reciprocity.

If the coaching techniques discussed above are done well, then there is a good chance that a spontaneous commitment will be forthcoming, and the need to elicit a promise will take care of itself. It's worth stressing, yet again, that a promise that doesn't come from within, spontaneously, probably isn't worth having anyway. If you do get a spontaneous promise, then simply thank the individual for it with as much warmth as you can. That internal promise might come at the end of a 'one to ten' coaching conversation about sleep, diet, exercise, and other wellbeing issues, but if it doesn't, then that's it, really.

It is, of course, only immediate risk and legality that eliciting a promise applies to, as there will be times when – if nothing else – the *law* requires you to point out a hazard or challenge an unsafe act or situation. In this situation, we do require a promise not to repeat the act/to take remedial action, and if that's the case, a little bit of psychology can help.

Other examples where a promise is required involve situations where a solution is 'high impact but high cost' and not likely to be addressed any time soon, if at all. You'll be aware of a thousand examples where this might be more complex than 'we simply haven't any money to invest'.

For example, you might find a problem with PPE compliance that is caused largely by on-going ventilation problems, which

DOI: 10.4324/9781003177784-9

themselves are caused by the design of a decrepit old building that's not really fit for its current purpose. You may well find yourselves discussing a range of solutions involving portable buildings, or temporary but expensive extraction systems, when someone will point out that the building is being closed in six months when everyone moves to the new buildings and the problem will be solved. Finding any meaningful amount of capital investment in this situation may prove close to impossible.

In such a case we really do have to fight a six-month guerrilla war as best we can, with what we have.

A SIMPLE BUT POWERFUL TIP WHEN A PROMISE *IS* NEEDED

Researchers such as Professor Robert Cialdini have found that if a person looks you in the eyes and says the 'I' word when making a promise, they are something like three times less likely to go on to break that promise. You don't want them looking at the ground and mumbling, 'Sure, no problem, I'm on it' or some such, which is just a grown-up version of crossing your fingers behind your back!

Imagine you're on a beach, and a complete stranger asks you to look after their belongings for five minutes whilst they get their children an ice cream. If you look them in the eye and say 'I will', how long will you keep an eye on their things? If they *never* come back for some reason, would you perhaps bundle the stuff up, hand it in somewhere, and leave a note under a stone telling them where to find it? Your altruistic perseverance is caused by an internal 'integrity' switch, which is subconsciously switched on when you (as children say) 'pinky promise'.

To look at this from the other side, how confident would you feel about leaving your possessions in the care of someone who avoids your eyes and mumbles 'sure' in the general direction of the sea?

So, when it comes to promises, the 'eyes' and the 'I's really do have it.

RECIPROCITY

Another hugely powerful tool of social behaviour is the unwritten 'law' of reciprocity. The behaviours it encourages are hugely biologically adaptive, and stem from early promises such as, 'I'll take my turn to try and kill a dinosaur – you don't eat all that's left of this one when I'm gone'. It's a fundamental building block of civilisation. Of course, some people try and take advantage of its power. Con artists and cults use this all the time by being 'nice', or by giving free gifts, and trying to oblige us to do something for them in return. (It's also why we get sent free pens by charities.)

Studies suggest that the 'fairness' concept is the most powerful of all social constructs, and popular culture provides any number of examples of its appeal. Marlon Brando's 'Godfather' and nearly every character played by Clint Eastwood, Mel Gibson, or Charles Bronson would fall into the 'harsh but *fair*' and thus broadly *admirable* category. We curse when we are unlucky, but we positively *seethe* when we are treated *unfairly*.

This helps explain why a workforce can spend years getting over the disappointment of an initiative that was launched but not followed through with, even though a lot of workforce time and effort was put into it. (Have you ever heard a workforce refer to 'another "**$**!! starburst" initiative' without inserting an oath or two in the middle?)

It is an excellent idea to always ask ourselves, 'If I were in their shoes, would I think this unfair?' In the face of what appears unreasonable indifference or cynicism, it's always worth asking if any unfairness is perceived – either at the time or previously. If there is, you have a serious motivational problem to address.

With reference to the design solutions that we discussed earlier in the book, the very best form of reciprocity is when we can say, 'If we get these suggestions implemented by the end of the month, will you come up with some more, please?'

After all, that seems fair.

SUMMARY OF KEY POINTS

- A promise made to the floor is at least three times as likely to be broken as a promise made using the word 'I' whilst looking you *in* the eye. On those occasions when you need someone to make you a promise, make sure it's a *'promise promise'*!
- Reciprocity is a hugely powerful cause of behaviour. A perception of unfairness very often explains what can seem unreasonably negative or even self-defeating behaviour. More positively, if addressed well, it can often lead to a 'virtuous circle'. Do *not* ever break promises.

BOB'S ATTEMPTS AT SINCERE PRAISE WERE STILL CONSIDERED A LITTLE OVER THE TOP IN THE FOUNDRY

CHAPTER 7

Close out

In this chapter I will discuss:

- Sincere thanks.
- SMART actions.
- Closing the loop.

In many respects, follow up is perhaps the most important section of all, because if you get your follow up wrong, much of what was right before that will be undone. However, there are really only a few things to remember.

SINCERE THANKS

Remember the huge power of positivity, and say 'thank you' for anything at all sensible that comes out of the discussion. Thank the person warmly and sincerely, too. As we've discussed, 85 per cent of a communication isn't in what we say, it's in how we say it. If you're going through the motions, they'll know you're insincere. On the other hand, a sincere thank you reinforces anything positive and makes it more likely next time.

You might even like to use former US President Bill Clinton's trick of making some sort of physical touch to add emphasis. Apparently how sincere he was trying to *appear to be* followed this system:

- Warm handshake.
- Warm handshake with left hand clasped over joined hands.
- Warm handshake with left hand clasped about forearm.
- Warm handshake with left hand clasped on shoulder.

 DOI: 10.4324/9781003177784-10

Some commentators said it correlated with how big a lie he was telling, and that the more 'sincerity' he put into it, the bigger the lie. I'm sure that's sheer cynicism, but you get the point! Whether or not Bill Clinton was telling the truth in every case, his 'touchy' approach worked very well for him. But it doesn't have to be so over the top. Anyone who's ever played sport knows that the slightest nod of the head in acknowledgement for something well done from the strong but silent 'hard man/woman' of the team can make you feel six inches taller. (This is, of course, important to note in a world where handshakes might not return for some time. I'm not sure how even Bill Clinton might finesse a fist or elbow bump!)

Regardless, one way or another, just let the person know you're appreciative – appropriately, and as sincerely as you can.

WHERE THE LEARNING REQUIRES A PLAN OF ACTION

Ideally, any agreements here will follow the famous SMART acronym:

- Specific.
- Measurable.
- Agreed.
- Realistic.
- Time-set.

The idea of the acronym is to make a realistic plan that is clear, specific, and can be followed. Perhaps the very first design solution I saw was at a chemical company, where people would 'quickly nip in' to a high-hazard area to check the reading on a gauge just inside a door without donning the required PPE. The job only took a few seconds, but donning the extensive PPE required several minutes.

The very simple action plan was:

> Get maintenance to confirm that the gauge can be moved to the outside wall. It shouldn't take more than an hour to do that.

Pete, you make sure the engineers have the required PPE now, so that ideally, they can scope the job today – safely! – and get it done tomorrow. There shouldn't be a problem, as they are in the middle of an ongoing planned maintenance programme, and I will add a half a day to that right now. Let me know by tomorrow lunchtime if there are any problems I haven't thought of. Ask them to let me know in Friday's review meeting at the latest that it's done, or the reason why it hasn't been, if it hasn't.

It's of course important to follow up with the person you delegated to, if the loop closes with them, to check, 'Did you sort out X and did you get back to Y afterwards to let them know how it turned out?' Unless it's all affirmative, don't let it go. The final chance to demonstrate your genuine commitment to safety and health excellence is by your persistence here.

GETTING BACK TO SOMEONE

The third technique is very simple to describe, but can be harder to do. If you say you'll follow something up and let someone know how that goes. then you *have to do so*. Rude Nike rules apply. Even a simple message such as, 'It seems it's a lot more complicated than it looks when you get into it; I'll update by the end of next week' is immeasurably better than what will be perceived as 'sweet *football association*'.

A BEST PRACTICE INVESTMENT: A PERSON WHOSE JOB IS TO COVER ALL THE WEAKNESSES

As we've made clear several times above, knowledge itself is no use at all if we don't make use of it. Feedback and communication are key to this process. We really don't care *how* a company does the things above or *who* does it – in good behavioural tradition, we just care that it gets done, gets done well, and gets done on time.

I'd like to suggest a role that can be done part-time (or even full-time in a big company) and that directly address the several major weaknesses we often see compromising the benefits of a good approach to safety and health.

We recommend that some of the workforce be trained up as human error champions. They'll need to understand the basic theories and principles, and this will require a few days of training. (But only a few days. Temptation analysis and the law of unintended consequences are hugely impactful, but aren't rocket science). They will also require a senior manager mentor who can clear blockages and OK the larger cheques. Once trained and empowered, their task is to:

- Be the first point of call for any ideas and suggestions that come out of a safety and health contact (to make it easy for the supervisor or manager).
- Liaise with all stakeholder parties as required. (Occupational health, training, safety, learning and development, etc).
- Be the first point of call for any worker who has an idea – just after a safety or health contact has taken place (or at any other time).
- Tell people what's happening and why – not just verbally, but via noticeboards and other media that all can see.
- Get back to anyone who was involved in making changes or improvements in the system to let them know what's happening, or at least explaining why, if nothing seems to be happening.
- Be consulted whenever a change occurs – even if the change is not anticipated to have a safety or health impact. (Or perhaps *especially* when it's not considered to have a safety or health impact.)
- Look at the hiring process from a safety and health perspective.
- Look at supplier selection and contracting from the same point of view.

- Be involved in the purchasing of equipment with a specific view on its use *in practise.*

And also:

- Running (or at least helping with) the ongoing *process* safety audits and any audits or processes with a human factor element (for example, exit interviews).

- Running an ongoing follow up audit of the safety leadership behaviours requested above.

You might like to think of them as the sweeper of 'unintended consequences'.

It's a simple idea. This role takes the inconvenience out of the process whenever possible to bridge the gap between good intentions and actions. Remember, designing out inconvenience proactively is always a good idea.

SUMMARY OF KEY POINTS

- Make sure to thank anyone involved sincerely, to show genuine gratitude for their input and also to help embed the behaviour.
- Make sure that enhancement plans are SMART – avoid vague instructions that allow any 'wriggle room'.
- Follow up to ensure the plan was followed, and give feedback as appropriate!
- If feasible, train up a dedicated individual whose job is to proactively address these points.

Conclusion

These safety and health talks are pretty simple. What you are trying to do is to communicate clearly the standards you expect, and to throw an appropriate leadership shadow to inspire safer behaviour by setting an example, empowering, and coaching. Done well, it's a key element of 'good work'. But most important of all is to learn why things aren't perfect, and to show your *genuine* commitment by applying those lessons whenever that's financially or logistically viable.

At the start of the book, I suggested that we get the health and safety standards we are prepared to accept, and that we communicate this with our leadership over and above compliance and process integrity.

By being out there talking about safety, health, and wellbeing, and using the information and learning, you demonstrate your commitment. By leading properly – setting a good example, listening, learning, coaching, engaging, and empowering – you inspire 'willing followers', and by working from a 'just culture' perspective, you enhance trust and fairness and learn how best to use your resources. The benefits of 'good work' are about so much more than a decent wage packet and being largely free from physical risk and discomfort. We all, one way or another, contribute to that all day every day.

It's very much easier said than done, of course – but it really isn't rocket science.

Final checklist

The following questions are provided as a simple reminder of the key points. If you are able to answer yes to the majority of them after a safety conversation, then I *guarantee* you'll have laid another brick in the wall of a strong safety culture.

- Were you able to get the person talking to you in a reasonably relaxed and natural way?
- Did it remain professional and focused, and not overly informal or 'matey'?
- Did you ask 'why' *curiously* about any issues seen or raised?
- Did you proactively ask, 'Anything slow, uncomfortable or inconvenient?' about doing the job safely?
- Did you ask, 'What do you need to be safe and healthy?'
- Did you top and tail with 'How are you?' (largely rhetorical) and 'How *are* you?' questions?
- Were you able to praise something you saw? Or did praise come naturally because you used a method such as the 'rate yourself one to ten' approach?
- Did you use a questioning coaching technique to get them to be the one to come up with the answer, and to consider 'what if?' situations?
- Were any promises made to you inclusive of the 'I' word, whilst looking you in the eye, and just after you promised to do something for them?
- Were any actions agreed upon SMART?
- Finally, do you agree that whether we're talking about following up SMART actions delegated, actions you've committed to yourself, or just getting out and undertaking a safety talk at all, RUDE NIKE RULES ALWAYS APPLY?

Suggested basic seven-items checklist

1 How do you rate your supervisor's 'care' for your welfare?

5   Often asks after my wellbeing, and certainly would if I looked down or a bit stressed and manic.

4

3   Would ask if I was acting unusually flat or manic.

2

1   Would never ask, no matter what!

2   How do you rate your supervisor's praise and feedback?

5   Often praises routine safe behaviour.

4

3   Rarely praises safe behaviour/praises only exceptional behaviour.

2

1   Never praises safe behaviour.

3   **How often does your supervisor coach rather than tell?**

5   Coaches by drawing out knowledge and options, whenever feasible.

4

3   Sometimes coaches by using questions rather than telling.

2

1   Never uses questioning or coaching techniques.

4   **How often does your supervisor lead by example in a positive way?**

5   Always leads by example positively.

4

3   Usually leads by example positively

2

1   Sometimes leads by example positively.

5 **How often does your supervisor involve and empower?**

    5 Involves and empowers in design and decision-making whenever viable.

    4

    3 Has involved and empowered, but also frequently misses chances to do so.

    2

    1 Rarely, if ever, involves the workforce in design and decision-making.

6 **How well does your supervisor use incidents to learn about improvement opportunities?**

    5 Always asks 'curious why' and 'what do you need?', and often asks 'anything slow or uncomfortable?' questions.

    4

    3 Often asks 'curious why' and 'what do you need?' questions, and sometimes asks 'anything slow or uncomfortable?' questions.

    2

    1 Rarely asks 'why' curiously. Almost never asks 'what do you need?' or 'anything inconvenient?' questions.

7 **How well does your supervisor follow up and close out safety actions?**

    5 Always follows up and ensures close-out, or communicates the reasons for any delay.

    4

    3 Quite good at following up and closing out safety and health related actions.

    2

    1 Poor at following up and closing out actions.

This basic list could, of course, be several times longer and more precisely behaviourally anchored. However, even with something this simple, if you systemically follow up these items so that an average score of, for example, 3.1 can be turned into a score of just 3.8, that will, **most definitely**, reflect a transformation in your safety culture.

Further reading

Broadbent, David. (2007) 'What Kind of Safety Leader are You?' Paper presented at the *National Health and Safety Conference, Auckland, New Zealand*.

Coyle, Daniel. (2018) *The Culture Code*. London: Random House Business.

Daniels, A. and Agnew, J. (2010) *Safe by Accident?* Atlanta: Performance Management Publications.

Dekker, S. (2008) *The Field Guide to Understanding Human Error*. Farnham: Ashgate.

Dweck, Carol. (2017) *Mindset*. New York: Robinson.

Edmondson, Amy. (2019) *The Fearless Organisation*. Hoboken, NJ: Wiley.

Geller, E.S. (2001) *The Psychology of Safety Handbook*. Florida: CRC Press.

Goldstein, N.J., Martin, S.J. and Cialdini, R.B. (2007) *Yes! 50 Secrets of Persuasion*. London: Profile Books.

Heinrich, H.W. (1959) *Industrial Accident Prevention: A Scientific Approach* (4th edn). New York: McGraw-Hill.

Hopkins, A. (2008) *Failure to Learn*. Sydney: CCH Australia.

Lencioni, Patrick. (2016) *The Ideal Team Player*. Hoboken, NJ: Jossey Bass.

Mandela, N. (1994) *Long Walk to Freedom*. London: Abacus.

Reason, J. (1997) *Managing the Risks of Organisational Accidents*. Farnham: Ashgate.

Reason, J. (2008) *The Human Contribution*. Farnham: Ashgate.

Syed, Matthew. (2011) *Bounce*. London: Fourth Estate.

Syed, Matthew. (2015) *Black Box Thinking*. London: John Murray.

Thaler, R.H. and Sunstein, C.R. (2009) *Nudge*. London: Penguin.

Vroom, V. (1992) *Management and Motivation*. London: Penguin.

Walker, Sam. (2017) *The Captain Class*. London: Ebury Press.

If you find the material in this book of interest can I recommend the following readable books – for a long journey or perhaps as the 'one non-fiction one' to be taken on holiday! None are directly referenced in the text but were in mind every time I mentioned 'unintended consequences' or 'why people do what they do'! (It's worth noting that the books by Lencioni, Syed, and Walker listed above are written to be read widely.)

Berne, E. (1964) *Games People Play (Transactional Analysis)*. London: Penguin.

Brown, D. (2007) *Tricks of the Mind*. London: 4 Books.

Gladwell, M. (2002) *The Tipping Point*. London: Penguin.

Gladwell, M. (2005) *Blink*. London: Penguin.

Hallinan, J.T. (2009) *Why We Make Mistakes*. New York: Broadway Books.

Levitt, S. and Dunbar, S. (2007) *Freakonomics*. London: Penguin.

Levitt, S. and Dunbar, S. (2010) *Super Freakonomics*. London: Penguin.

McFarlin, B. (2004) *Drop the Pink Elephant*. Chichester: Capstone.

Index

Note: numbers in *italics* indicate a figure

121